Desalination
Water for the World's Future

Roy Popkin

FOREWORD BY
STEWART L. UDALL

FREDERICK A. PRAEGER, *Publishers*
New York • Washington • London

FREDERICK A. PRAEGER, PUBLISHERS
111 Fourth Avenue, New York, N.Y. 10003, U.S.A.
5, Cromwell Place, London S.W.7, England

Published in the United States of America in 1968
by Frederick A. Praeger, Inc., Publishers
© 1968 by Frederick A. Praeger, Inc.

Library of Congress Catalog Card Number: 68–16091

Printed in the United States of America

To Dorothy, the only wife I know
who would travel 7,000 miles to take
a picture of a desalination plant for
a husband back at the typewriter

Foreword

After centuries of effort with only limited success, man has learned in the past two decades how to convert large amounts of salt water into fresh water at relatively low cost. The various desalting processes are many; some, of considerable complexity. But they underscore a simple fact: We must develop additional water supplies to meet the exploding demands of home, factory, and farm.

For many areas, survival itself depends upon how well we utilize our scientific skills in desalting vast quantities of sea and inland brackish waters. In recent years, we have achieved significant break-throughs. Today, the use of nuclear energy holds great promise as a power source for low-cost desalination.

The quest for potable water is by no means confined to the United States. It is a world-wide problem of challenging proportions; fortunately, as desalting technology is developed and improved upon through research and experimentation, the data are shared among nations.

In these pages, Roy Popkin traces the advancement of desalination, from ancient times to modern. His projection of the exciting possibilities of salt-water conversion should go far toward creating among world citizens understanding of the technology, its costs, and the hope it holds for the years ahead.

STEWART L. UDALL

U. S. Secretary of the Interior

Washington, D.C.
May, 1968

Preface

It may seem odd to start a book about the social and economic aspects of desalination—or desalting, to use the increasingly favored short form—with a personal note. But the need for water is intensely personal. Without water, human beings cannot survive. Nor can nations.

So I begin with a few words about my uncle Sascha Koussewitzky. He lives in Israel—and has lived there since the days of the British mandate. Some years ago, he worked in the burning sun of the barren, rocky Negev desert, laying pipelines to bring water into a hitherto worthless part of the world. The pick he swung with what must have been backbreaking ardor helped bring a desert to life and make a new nation socially and economically viable. Today—partly because of his labors in an arid wasteland—he, my aunt, their son and daughter-in-law, and their young grandchildren have the water and food they need.

Water shortages exist in many parts of the world. There are places where population expansion is outstripping the availability of food and of usable fresh water, lands where misuse of water by waste and pollution is creating shortages that need not exist, lands where growth and expansion cannot take place until new or expanded supplies of water are found for human consumption, for industry, and for growing food. Other areas are just plain running dry.

The problem is stated in many ways, but all mean the same

thing: The world is facing a water crisis. How big is the problem? No one can measure it in exact quantities of gallons or acre-feet of water that will be needed in 1970 or 1975 or the year 2000, although it has been estimated that the United States alone will require 1 trillion gallons of water each day by the end of the current century—almost three times the amount used in 1960.

In mid-1967, Frank C. DiLuzio, then Assistant Secretary of the Interior for Water Pollution Control, and former director of the Office of Saline Water (OSW), spoke to an International Conference on Water for Peace. This gathering— the largest international conference ever held in Washington, D.C.—brought together almost 5,000 government leaders and water planners, representing more than seventy nations. For this audience of people with water problems, DiLuzio sounded a note of urgency with the statement: "Limited supplies of water are on a collision course with ever increasing demands. In parts of the world the collision has occurred with devastating results."

Droughts in India and water scarcity in the Middle East and other parts of the world are problems of today and, for many people, a life-and-death matter. The problems of tomorrow may be serious ones for many more people. For example, Israel has the water it needs today, but it is now using about 90 per cent of the water available within its borders, plus some relatively small amounts from the sea. By the early 1970's, in spite of one of the world's most exacting programs of controlling water management and use, Israel will be using all the water it has. Already, this tiny developing nation is so conscious of the value of water that, when an unexpectedly rainy and snowy spring in 1967 caused the reservoir at Lake Tiberias (the Sea of Galilee) to overflow—wasting water—the *Jerusalem Post* report of the event was almost apologetic in tone.

In the United States, as in Israel, today's water problems

can be expected to worsen in the years to come. The Southwest is running out of water. Right now, it is using all the water it can take legally—under interstate agreements and international pacts with Mexico—from the Colorado and Rio Grande rivers. Southwestern ranchers and farmers and municipalities are mining underground water to the point where there may soon be little or no underground water left to pump.

As the world nears the halfway year of the International Hydrological Decade, sponsored by the United Nations, which has as its goals the identification of global water resources and the development of technologies to make those resources available to people, industry, and agriculture, the direct, individual needs of people for water are still relatively small. They range from a few gallons a day in underdeveloped societies to a hundred gallons or more a day, perhaps, in societies where people have indoor plumbing, air conditioning, washing machines, dishwashers, and a seemingly unlimited supply of water to use and waste as they please. But there are far greater needs of industry—which are also, indirectly, the needs of people. And there are the large-scale needs of agriculture. If the world population doubles by the turn of the century—as has been predicted—the need for water to grow food will be critical.

Sea and brackish water can be made safe to drink and usable for farming and industry by desalting. (The hydrological cycle itself is a form of desalination, as salt water evaporates from the surface of the oceans, returns to earth as fresh water, and eventually finds its way back to the salty seas.) The words desalination and desalting appear with increasing frequency in the newspapers. One writer has called the process a "here and now" technology. However, no one involved with the technology would, at this point, be rash enough to predict that desalting alone can close the gap between water supply and water need. What is possible is that desalination technology can totally solve some water problems, help solve some others, and be applied extensively to improve the quality of inland surface and underground waters now unfit for ordinary use because they are too salty or otherwise mineralized or contaminated by such substances as mine acids. Development and improvement of several desalting methods will, undoubtedly, enable desalination to play an important role in greater utilization of traditional nonoceanic water resources, thereby adding a tremendous source of water to the world's supply.

There are many who question the role of desalination in solving present and future water problems, claiming that desalted water costs too much. Current controversies over desalination revolve around need and value versus costs.

This book attempts to provide a review of desalination today, where it may be going, what its real costs and real values may be in different kinds of circumstances, and how it may be related to other water-supply plans available on a long- or short-term basis. It offers some suggestions on how to go about evaluating the role desalting might play in the solution of local, national, or regional water problems. For more specific advice, water planners need the services of consulting engineers—hydrologists, geologists, agronomists, municipal planners, conservationists. Economists, too—those with a long view—will be needed, for the economics of water supply in general and desalting in particular is the economics of human survival.

ROY POPKIN

Garrett Park, Maryland
April, 1968

Acknowledgments

Many people helped in this quest for knowledge about desalination. To list them all would be well-nigh impossible, but those who provided major assistance included:

Frank C. DiLuzio, then Assistant Secretary of the Interior for Water Pollution Control; Dr. Jack A. Hunter, Director of the Office of Saline Water (OSW); Pat O'Meara, Information Officer for the OSW, and others of the OSW staff, including Walter L. Barnes, at the time manager of the Wrightsville Beach, N.C., research center and now chief of the Plant Engineering Division, and Wilfred B. Hahn, present manager of the Wrightsville Beach facilities.

Also, Harlan Wood, Information Officer, International Conference on Water for Peace; Dr. P. A. Mawer, Plant Process Division, Water Research Association, United Kingdom, and several of his associates; Dr. Robert Passino, Consiglio Nazionale delle Ricerche, Rome, Italy; Professor A. A. Delyannis, Athens, Greece; the Honorable Abram Harman, former Ambassador of Israel, and his science adviser, Hillel Aldaag; His Royal Highness, Prince Mohamed Al Faisal, Director, Saline Water Conversion Office, Saudi Arabia; Masatoshi Kuwahara, Councilor, Public Utility Board, Kanagawa Prefecture, Yokohama, Japan; Dr. Joseph Barnea, Resources and Transport Division, United Nations; Dr. D. A. Denton, Howard Florey Research Laboratory, University of Melbourne, Victoria, Australia; Dr. D. R. Anand, Minister of

xiii

Water and Electricity, India, and D. Bhushan of the Directorate of Research Coordination and Industrial Liaison, India; C. H. van Vierssen, Scientific Attaché, Royal Netherlands Embassy.

Also, E. A. Cadwallader, Chief, Chemical Division, Office of Engineering, Agency for International Development, and U.S. Department of Agriculture Agricultural Research Service officials; Dr. C. A. Bower, Director, Salinity Laboratory, Riverside California; Dr. J. R. Furr, Research Horticulturist, Date and Citrus Station, Indio, California; John R. Turner, Cotton Research Station, Shafter, California; and P. A. Putnam, Nutrition and Management Investigations, Animal Husbandry Research Division, Beltsville, Maryland.

Others who contributed generously were Dr. Wilburn G. Schroeder, University of Maryland; Mr. Wilson Radway, Special Projects Director, Church World Service; Mrs. Helen Rossi of the *Jerusalem Post;* Mrs. Helen Decker, of the U.S. Information Agency; Joseph R. Wilson, Manager, Desalting Engineering Development, Kaiser Engineers; Glendon E. Rose, Director of Marketing, Water Processing Division, Aerojet-General Corporation; C. A. Tidball, Baldwin-Lima-Hamilton Corporation; Harvey Shipman, Westinghouse Corporation; David S. Goodman, representing Aqua-Chem, Inc.; James L. Appleton, Bechtel Corporation; Robert P. Will, Legislative Representative, The Metropolitan Water District of Southern California; and the librarians of the Department of the Interior and the Garrett Park Branch of the Montgomery County, Maryland, Public Library.

Many of the above have been and will be intimately involved in the future of desalination in many parts of the world. Their assistance is gratefully acknowledged. I hope this book will contribute to public understanding of what they are trying to achieve for mankind.

                                          R. P.

Contents

Desalination
WATER FOR THE WORLD'S FUTURE

1

Desalination: The State of the Art

Man's interest in desalting the seas goes back a long way. In the fourth century B.C., Aristotle described a method of evaporating sea water to produce drinking water. Greek sailors of his day drank fresh water desalted on board ship, as the seamen of many countries have done for centuries since. But not until the invention of the steamboat created a need for evaporators to provide noncorrosive water supplies for ships' boilers did attempts to make saline water fresh emphasize quantity. Today, modern ocean liners and warships can produce as much as 450,000 gallons of fresh water daily with on-board evaporators.

There were several early methods of desalination, including the use of wick siphons to pass salt water through threads of wool, which trapped the salts. In the first century A.D., the Romans experimented with the filtering of sea water through clayey soil. By the fourth century, distillation had become common as a means of desalting sea water. St. Basil, a Greek religious leader, wrote, "Sailors boil sea water, collecting the vapor in sponges, to quench their thirst in pressing needs."

The first known treatise on distillation was written by an Arabian chemist in the eighth century. In the 1500's, one writer offered four methods of sweetening sea water: "by filtering through sand; by clean linen laid over a boiler and squeezing the moisture out, as from sponges; by distillation; and also by bowls made from white virgin wax, which 'tis said

3

will free the water from its saltiness and from some parts of its nauseous bitter."

The first known patent for a desalination process was granted in England in 1869, and the first steam distillation process used on land was built at Aden by the British Government in 1869 to supply fresh water to vessels stopping at the port.

In the New World, American scientist-statesman Thomas Jefferson, with his characteristic interest in everything, presented a method of shipboard distillation to American sea captains, but the first large, land-based desalting unit was not built until 1930. Then, Griscom-Russell, an American firm later absorbed by Baldwin-Lima-Hamilton, erected a plant in Aruba, in the Netherlands Antilles. It produced 625,000 gallons of fresh water daily and was the forerunner of the many large-quantity desalting plants now in use in other arid parts of the world.

Desalting technology, in crude and in increasingly sophisticated forms, was for many years used primarily with sea water. Much of the development related to the needs of men and ships on the high seas, but the early Romans and, later, the people of the Netherlands Antilles also turned to the sea as a source of fresh water for use on land.

One of the great paradoxes of the world water problem is that most of the water on earth is in the oceans. The following table, based on U.S. Geological Survey estimates, shows how the world's water supply is distributed:

Location	Water Volume (in cubic miles)	Per Cent of Total Water
Fresh-water lakes	30,000	0.009
Saline lakes and inland seas	25,000	0.008
Average in rivers and streams	300	0.0001
Soil moisture and near-surface ground water	16,000	0.005
Deeper ground water	2,000,000	0.61
Icecaps and glaciers	7,000,000	2.15
Atmosphere	3,100	0.0001
Oceans	317,000,000	97.2

The oceans, which cover 70 per cent of the earth and contain all but 2.8 per cent of its water, contain such a high concentration of sodium and magnesium in their waters that this inexhaustible supply is—all of it—unfit to drink. The drinking of sea water aggravates thirst and leads to convulsions, delirium, and eventually malfunction of the kidneys and death. Sea water is also unsatisfactory for most industrial processes and, as far as we now know, can be used in agriculture only under very limited conditions.

There are no figures to show how much of that 2.8 per cent of the world's water on or under the ground is polluted, too brackish for use, or so deeply embedded in rock structure under ground that it would be impossible to bring it to the surface. Ground water located and pumped up from more than a quarter of a mile below the Saudi Arabian deserts recently proved too salty to use without treatment.

Today's growing water-supply crisis is compounded not only by massive demand but also by increased pollution and mineralization of rivers, lakes, and underground resources. Population adds vast amounts of wastes—including salts—to surface and underground waters. Great rivers, such as the Colorado and the Rhine, for example, have become saltier and saltier. Their downstream waters are less and less potable, a fact that Mexico and the Netherlands have learned the hard way. Overpumping of ground waters also creates future problems, and evaporation takes a considerable portion of the surface waters in land areas and puts them back into the endless hydrological cycle. Only a small amount of the water that falls back to earth is captured or frozen into the polar icecap regions. Irrigation, too, creates difficulties; the leaching action of the irrigation water that is not transpired through growing plants moves down through the soil, carrying salts and other minerals, which are deposited in underground waters or eventually drain into rivers and lakes. Thousands of communities throughout the world are drinking brackish water because of natural pollution, if it can be called that, while others, in mining areas particularly, find their water supply polluted by mine acids.

Yet, sea water and brackish water can be made safe to drink and usable for farming and industry with the application of present-day desalination technology—and on a scale not even dreamed of in the 1930's, when the first large plant went into use.

Recent Advances

Perhaps the most important modern advance in desalination technology was the development of the principle of multistage flash distillation in the early 1950's. This method, which will be described later in this chapter, has become the cornerstone for the big new multimillion-gallons-per-day desalting plants now in operation or being built or planned in many parts of the world. Reverse-osmosis techniques hold great promise for use in inland areas and for waste treatment. Many different kinds of workable desalting technologies are in use or development, and the coupling of desalination plants with nuclear energy as a source of heat for the distillation process gives promise of greater economy and cheaper fresh water. A nuclear-powered, 150-million-gallons-per-day (MGD) plant planned for the Metropolitan Water District (MWD) at Los Angeles will provide fresh water at the highly competitive price of under 25 cents per 1,000 gallons. Comparable nuclear-powered units are projected for Israel and the Soviet Union.

Interestingly, some of the more grandiose water-supply schemes advanced in recent years also depend upon some form of basic desalination. Two of the proposals involve the damming of large bodies of water—Long Island Sound, on the East Coast of the United States, and the Mediterranean Sea. These schemes would turn bodies of salt water into fresh water by a long-term program of dilution and salt removal. Eventually, they would become gigantic rain- and river-fed fresh-water reservoirs. A third scheme, to dig a canal from the Mediterranean to a large depressed area in the Sahara Desert, would create a vast inland sea from the surface of which the hot African sun would evaporate large quantities of water vapor, which would turn to rain naturally or as the result of cloud seeding. Competent engineers say those proposals are technically feasible. Their physical and political practicality, however, is problematical. They are mentioned here to illustrate that some forms of desalination technology might some day be applied on a fantastically large scale.

Although the largest plants actually functioning as this is written are producing only about 3 MGD, desalination technology and its application in the actual production of fresh water is developing rapidly. Construction of a 7.5-MGD plant for Tijuana, Mexico, has begun; a plant of similar size is being built in the Netherlands; and the initial work has been started on the first units to provide design information for the Los Angeles plant. Israel and the United States have completed a feasibility study for a 100-MGD plant on the Mediterranean, and Israel is negotiating for its financing. The Soviet Union is preparing to build a 125-MGD plant on the Caspian Sea. Like so many of the smaller facilities being built today, these large plants will serve a dual purpose, providing both electricity and fresh water.

And Dr. Jack Hunter, Director of the U.S. Office of Saline Water (OSW), at the conclusion of the initial study by a joint U.S.–Mexican commission of the feasibility of desalting as a solution for some of the water problems in northern Mexico and the southwestern United States, said that a 1,000-MGD plant could and should be built on the Gulf of California to provide fresh water for both countries.

Such progress has been made or is anticipated, in spite of the fact that many people in the water field today are still inclined to shrug off desalting as an expensive technology with only limited application. One of the standard works on water supply, *Water and Man: A Study in Ecology,* a compendium of opinion published in 1950, did not mention desalination. (It did show a certain lack of imagination in predicting that Americans would never accept air conditioning because it made rooms too clammy.) Ten years later, The RAND Corporation's *Water Supply, Economics, Technology and Policy,* published by the University of Chicago Press, stated bluntly that "the possibilities for sea-water conversion are overblown . . . nothing so far in the laboratory gives any indication of promising a source of supply by conversion for municipal, and certainly not for irrigation, use at costs that approach those of many other technical and economic alternatives." The RAND Corporation compounded poor prophecy by concluding that "none of the presently conceived processes is likely to be chosen as a source of water in any significant amount for any purpose within the United States for many years to come."

What The RAND Corporation experts seem to have overlooked was the potential of multistage flash distillation, although the process had been perfected at the time the book was published. Their failure as prophets was underlined dramatically in 1967, when the city of Key West, Florida, began receiving 2.6 million gallons of fresh water daily from a desalting plant. The plant was built as an alternative to a 131-mile aqueduct, which had let the city down badly in the spring of that year, when Florida suffered a serious drought and Key West had to ration its water.

One of the best prophets of the middle 1950's was David S. Jenkins, first director of the Office of Saline Water after it was created by Congress in 1952. He was a co-author of an article on desalination for the *1955 Yearbook of Agriculture,* published by the U.S. Department of Agriculture, which discussed the possibility that fresh water from the sea could be produced at costs attractive for irrigation use, and said that "continuing research and development work are bringing us closer and closer to such a reality." The article noted that there were already many installations providing fresh water in sufficient quantity to permit the profitable functioning of industries which, "without such conversion, probably could not exist." The article also suggested that heat from nuclear reactor plants could be used in various desalting processes.

Desalination proponents know the big plants will work. Dr. Hunter, for example, and many engineers in the field, see no reason to doubt that 1,000-MGD plants can be built and operated successfully and economically in many places. On January 1, 1967, there were only about 600 functioning desalting plants with a daily capacity of 25,000 gallons or more throughout the world, and it is presently estimated that there will not be a total of 1,000-MGD capacity—the equivalent of just one of the projected giant-sized plants—before the end of the next decade. But this conservative prediction does not take into account the growing awareness and application of the technology involved, perhaps because, as Secretary of the Interior Stewart L. Udall said in 1967 at the International Conference on Water for Peace, in Washington, D.C., "the science and technology of water management, with some notable exceptions in the areas of flood control and desalination, still move at little better than a glacial pace." Although it is generally accepted in the field that it takes between twenty and thirty years to plan, get political approval for, finance, and build an extensive waterworks program of more than strictly local nature, there is reason to hope that the pace will increase.

Desalting Now

Just where does desalting stand today? What is the state of the art? In its January, 1967, issue of *Resources,* the nonprofit organization Resources for the Future (financed by the Ford Foundation to advance the development, conservation, and use of natural resources through research and education) reported the then current desalination capacity at about 50 MGD in the form of large land-based plants, "an increase of 100 per cent in the past two years."

The report noted that there was strong competition between American and British manufacturers for the sale of desalting plants, with the United States accounting for about 40 per cent of the sales. Since then, one Wisconsin manufacturer alone has reported orders amounting to about 45 per cent of the installed or projected capacity. Major techniques in use, according to the *Resources* report, were flash distillation, electrodialysis, and vapor compression. The report reviewed British Water Research Association analyses, which concluded that the big world market for desalting plants "will be in the small-to-medium range, with plants not exceeding 15 MGD."

Touching on an important potential use of desalting technology in relation to water pollution, the report said that electrodialysis was being used in the Federal Water Pollution Control Administration's water renovation pilot plant at Lebanon, Ohio, where municipal sewage, after secondary treatment, goes through a desalting unit that removes 300 parts per million (PPM) of the dissolved salts from the 700 left in the water, thus meeting U.S. Public Health Service standards.

Trade papers in the water-supply field predict that world desalting expenditures will be $2.1 billion between 1967 and 1975—$950 million for plant construction, $500 million for associated steam and power facilities, and $680 million for research and development. The bulk of the research and development money will come from the U.S. Office of Saline Water and the Atomic Energy Commission (AEC), while the rest will come largely from the governments of Israel, the

United Kingdom, Japan, the U.S.S.R., and West Germany. Of the predicted 1-billion-gallon capacity expected to be in use by the late 1970's, 85 per cent is expected to be for sea-water conversion, with most of the capacity in plants producing 50 MGD, or more, or in plants producing 1–10 MGD.

Generally, water containing less than 1,000 parts of salt per million parts of water is considered fresh. Brackish water ranges from 1,000 PPM to 35,000 PPM. Sea water ordinarily has 35,000 PPM, or more. Bodies of water such as the Great Salt Lake and the Dead Sea have even higher levels of salt, running as high as 250,000 PPM. The U.S. Public Health Services sets 500 PPM as the top limit acceptable for drinking water; some industrial processes require almost zero PPM.

Industrial exhibitors at the International Conference on Water for Peace displayed a wide variety of desalting methods. Eight companies showed equipment for reverse-osmosis processes—a major accomplishment, since this particular technology was barely out of the research laboratory in the early 1960's. But unless there is some unexpected technology break-through, it is assumed that multistage flash distillation will be this century's most widely used process for converting sea water—outdistancing other methods such as long-tube evaporation or vapor compression. Brackish-water conversion plants will utilize reverse-osmosis or electrodialysis methods.

Terms like reverse osmosis, electrodialysis, long-tube evaporation, multistage flash distillation, and the like may be strange to many readers, but they are already familiar in many parts of the world. The U.N. report of desalting projects in 1966 alone showed fifty-four completed, approved, under construction, or planned. These ranged from small solar distillation plants in Greece, Portugal, and Australia to million- or multimillion-gallons-per-day multistage flash plants in Israel, Kuwait, the United Arab Republic, Saudi Arabia, the Virgin Islands, Malta, Mexico, Italy, Spain, the U.S.S.R., and the United States. Other countries on the list of smaller projects included Libya, Mauritania, Tunisia, Iran, Oman, Antigua, Bermuda, Brazil, Peru, West Germany, Spanish Sahara, the United Kingdom, and Australia. Total potential capacity represented more than seven times the existing capacity reported at the end of the same year.

The Processes Explained

Perhaps it would be well at this point to describe the thirteen desalting processes now in use or under development, for they will be referred to repeatedly in many contexts throughout the ensuing chapters. The principal sea- or brackish-water conversion processes can be divided into five basic classifications: distillation, membrane, humidification, freezing, and chemical.

The most widely used today are the distillation processes, which utilize a method of separating fresh water from salt water that goes back into antiquity. When salt water is boiled, the salt remains behind while the fresh water boils off as vapor. In desalting conversion processes, the vapor is cooled to condense the fresh-water steam. This means that each of the following distillation methods involves first heating the salt or brackish water to a temperature higher than boiling point so that it will turn to steam and then cooling the steam.

Long-tube vertical distillation is a process in which the salt water falls through long metal tubes inside a large chamber filled with steam. The exchange of heat between the steam in the chamber and the colder water in the tubes turns some of the cold water to steam and at the same time condenses some of the steam as it cools off. For efficient use of the heat energy, the process is repeated in a series of chambers, with the steam from one heating the cold brine flowing through tubes in the next before it is condensed into fresh water. The portion of the heated salt water that does not evaporate flows into the next series of tubes in the next chamber, where it is heated again by steam at progressively lower pressures, which permit the heated water to vaporize into steam at lower temperatures. In the Office of Saline Water's experimental plant at Freeport, Texas, the sea water enters the first chamber at 250° F., the last at 115° F. The separate chambers are called "effects," so this process is often described as long-tube vertical multiple-effect distillation.

Multistage flash distillation, which is expected to be the work horse of large-scale desalting for the next decade or more, also capitalizes on the fact that water boils at lower temperatures as it is subjected to lower pressures. In this process, the sea water is heated and then flows into a chamber where the pressure is low enough to make some of the water boil instantly, or "flash," into steam. This steam is condensed into fresh water by the unheated sea water flowing in coils through each chamber on its way to the heating unit. When some of the water turns to steam, the temperature of the remaining brine is lowered before it flows into the next unit, where the pressure is lower and it again flashes into steam. This process, repeated through a series of chambers, makes maximum use of the heat energy added to the salt water before it enters the first chamber, because 90 per cent of that heat is transferred to the incoming colder water as it moves through the condenser units in each chamber.

Multi-effect, multistage distillation takes advantage of the fact that flash distillation is more efficient if the number of stages used for vaporizing and preheating the sea water increases. It uses a series of effects by breaking up the single circulating path of the multistage flash process into several circulating loops. The separation of the process into a series of effects permits better control of scale treatment, the use of smaller temperature changes, lower-cost pretreatment of the intake water, reduction of required heat-transfer surfaces, and over-all improvement in efficiency.

Vapor compression distillation is a process in which vapor created by an initial heating source is further heated by mechanical compression to raise the temperature and pressure of the steam, which is then used to heat sea water coming into subsequent effects. Some of this water vaporizes and is re-used to heat the brine coming into the first effect. In both effects, some of the heated vapor condenses into fresh water, which falls to the bottom and is pumped off. In this process, most of the energy involved is used by the compressor motor rather than for heating the salt water itself.

The membrane processes are also extensively used today, but generally with inland brackish waters whose salt or mineral content is considerably lower than that of sea water. There are major differences among the three membrane processes, although all use a thin filmlike sheet—much like the sheets used in stage lighting—that acts as a filter, allowing fresh water to flow through but keeping out the salts.

Electrodialysis is the most highly developed of the membrane processes, but it is expensive. It utilizes the fact that salt is composed of sodium and chloride, which separate in solution into positive and negative ions that can be forced by an electric charge to move through separate filters—one of which permits the positive sodium ion to pass, the other the negative chloride ion. Fresh, saltless water is left between the two membranes to be pumped out. The higher the amount of salt, the more electricity required, limiting the application, because of the cost of electric power, largely to brackish waters. If the cost of both membranes and other equipment can be reduced far enough, electrodialysis is expected to become economically feasible for sea-water desalting, but only where cheap electric power is available.

Electrodialysis has to be more flexible than distillation processes, for there is a higher degree of variability in the content of brackish water than in sea water, so that many of the steps involved in the complete process are changeable in relation to the specific degree of mineralization involved.

Transport depletion is a form of electrodialysis using non-selective membranes to screen out positive ions and one selective membrane for negative ions. Elimination of the positive, or anion, membranes, which deteriorate rapidly, means a saving in costs. This process is based on the difference in speed of ions moving in solution as compared to the movement in membranes. The negative ions (cations) move through the membrane faster than they are diffused into the solution, resulting in the formation of areas of the cell where there are few, if any, sodium and chloride ions. From these areas, fresh water is drawn off. Transport depletion is subject to the same general advantages and limitations as electrodialysis.

Reverse osmosis is a relatively new and highly promising process. It reverses nature's osmotic pressure, which causes liquids to flow through a semipermeable membrane. (The human body, for example, is loaded with membrane processes; man's water balance is controlled automatically by the osmotic pressure of the blood. Ocean fish assimilate fresh water through natural membranes.) When saline water and fresh water are separated by a semipermeable membrane, osmosis will cause the fresh water to flow through the membrane into salt water. But if pressure greater than the natural osmotic force is applied to the salty or mineralized water, the process is reversed, forcing the water in the brine through the membrane to the fresh-water side while the concentrated salts of minerals remain behind. Because this process is relatively simple and requires little energy—no heat is involved—it holds hope for great economy in the treatment of brackish water and, perhaps some day, large amounts of sea water.

The two humidification processes are quite different from each other.

Solar humidification relies on nature to do most of the work. In essence, the heat from the sun evaporates vapor from the surface of the salt water. The vapor then condenses on a glass or plastic cover of the solar still and slides down into troughs, through which it is carried off as fresh water. The sun's rays passing through the glass or plastic do not lose their heat until they reach the surface of the water, where the heat loss raises the temperature of the water. (The same natural process can be seen at work in greenhouses.) Although there is an obvious economic advantage in the use of "free" heat energy, the process requires sunny days and a large amount of water surface to produce an appreciable amount of fresh water.

In *diffusion humidification,* the water passes through disks rotating through the pool of saline water. As the disks rotate, some water adheres to their surface, from which it evaporates. The vapor diffuses between the disks and stationary plates placed between them and, as it cools on the stationary plates, runs down their sides into troughs. Although this process requires less surface space than solar humidification, it does require energy to rotate the disks and heat the water to increase the relative humidity and enhance the condensation rate. It has good potential for small-scale applications such as domestic, restaurant, and hotel use.

Two freezing processes show considerable promise and are already being used on a limited basis. These processes utilize the fact that when salt water is frozen, fresh-water ice crystals are formed, while the salt remains in the unfrozen solution. Here, as in distillation, both cooling and heating steps are required.

In the *direct freezing* process, the salt water flows into a vacuum chamber. Part of the water vaporizes because of the low pressure, while about half is frozen into ice crystals. The mixture of crystals and brine—called "slurry"—is pumped to the bottom of a separation column, where the ice crystals flow to the top and are separated from the slurry and melted down into fresh water. At the same time, the vapor is ultimately condensed by distillation and becomes part of the fresh-water product.

In *secondary refrigerant freezing*, a refrigerant such as butane is used instead of the vacuum freezing method. Under compression, the butane is also used as part of the ice-melting process to produce the fresh water.

There are two other processes, both chemical, now being developed.

The *ion-exchange method* uses a porous bed of materials that can exchange ions with those in solution that touches the bed. In this process, two beds are used to draw off the sodium and chloride ions and leave only fresh water. Because of the expense of regenerating the resin beds, which weaken progressively until they lose their ion-exchange capability, this process has only limited application at present. It is thought to have a good potential for converting low-salt-content brackish water, but it has also been used for small amounts of sea water. One practical use is in emergency kits for life rafts.

The *hydrate method,* now under extensive research and experimentation, combines saline water with a hydrating agent such as propane or carbon dioxide in a reactor. In the reactor, under the right pressure and temperature, hydrate crystals containing only pure water are formed. These are separated from the brine, washed, and melted. The water and the hydrating agent become two distinct liquids, which, like oil and water, will not mix and can be separated.

Against this background of widely different processes, some of which are already producing millions of gallons of fresh water daily, it is difficult to assess predictions for the future with any degree of accuracy. If Dr. Hunter's recommended 1,000-MGD plant should be built in the next few years—and it may very well be, because the water is so sorely needed in the areas it would supply—the capacity predicted for the late 1970's would be doubled by just that one project.

One might say that modern desalting technology is having a robust adolescence. Its infancy in the early 1930's, when the first large-scale land-based plants were constructed, was relatively quiet. Its adolescence is typically unpredictable and flamboyant. Like the automobile industry, it has produced a multitude of styles, shapes, models, sizes, and colors.

At the 1967 International Conference on Water for Peace, there were displays of actual or mock-up desalination plants, running all the way from one-man, lifeboat-sized packets to models of nuclear-powered 150-MGD plants covering twenty-five acres or so. One demonstration plant actually produced 10,000 gallons of pure water daily. There were plants to put on ships and a ship that was designed to be a floating desalting plant; portable plants, run by small gasoline or diesel engines, that could be hooked up to supply a single motel by providing fresh water from a local brackish source; plants that could be put on railroad flatcars or trucks, or towed behind trucks like trailers. One firm distributed a pocket-sized, do-it-yourself reverse-osmosis kit, and another had mimeographed forms—in English and Spanish—for a partial do-it-yourself analysis of a community's water problems, to be used in connection with the request for information about the firm's electrodialysis unit. The form included a box that the prospective purchaser could check if he wanted a free plastic bottle in which to send water samples to the firm's headquarters for a free analysis of mineral content.

Does all this mean that one can really rush down to his

neighborhood manufacturer, get a free water analysis, and walk out with a carbon copy of a signed contract for a desalination plant that will help solve his water problems? The answer is a qualified yes—if one wants a small, self-contained unit for use in connection with a small business, small farm, home, or relatively small town.

And bigger things are in sight.

John W. Simpson, a Westinghouse Electric Corporation vice president, recently assured a U.S. Senate subcommittee of the Interior and Insular Affairs Committee:

> We are prepared to submit a *firm bid* on a large desalting plant at this time—50 million gallons per day, or 100 million, or 150 million, or larger is desired. . . . Construction of this plant would begin *immediately*. We will submit this bid on a turn-key firm-price basis, with warranted capacity, warranted heat rate, warranted power consumption, warranted chemical consumption, warranted purity and completion date. If the customer desires, we will also operate the water desalting plant for him. This ties down all the factors that go into determining the cost of producing water. In our opinion, the cost of water from a plant on these terms can satisfy real and present needs in certain areas of the world today.

Gordon F. Leitner, Executive Vice President of Aqua-Chem, Inc., speaking before the National Instrument Society of America in mid-1967, said:

> This process [desalting] is by far the biggest and most dramatic solution to the water problem for seacoast communities, and growth figures in the industry prove it. Just a few years ago the desalting equipment industry was predicting a total of 200-million-gallons-per-day capacity by 1972. Today it is seen as topping a billion gallons per day by then.

Additional support for the statements that at least some desalting technologies are already available for large-scale use comes from Dr. Hunter. Hunter came to the Office of Saline Water from the aerospace industry, where his last assignment was to spend a year investigating new fields in which his firm could anticipate sales of $1 billion a year or more. After thorough investigation, he selected desalination as such a field. Reviewing recent developments in desalting technology at the International Conference on Water for' Peace, Dr. Hunter said, "We are at the stage where certain process technologies are ready to be employed on a large-scale basis. Other processes are under active development with an ultimate goal of achieving economically acceptable desalting systems for any world location."

Soviet scientists further emphasize both the current readiness of some of the technologies and the need for their application in the immediate or near future. Professor Vitaly Klyachko of the All-Union Research Institute for Water Supply, Sewage, Hydraulic Structures, and Engineering Hydrology maintains it is "technically possible today to desalt water on any scale," and estimates that some 10 to 12 thousand electrodialysis units will be needed in the next few years to provide water for small state-farm settlements and villages in the southeastern parts of the Soviet Union. Vasily Yemelyanov of the U.S.S.R. Academy of Sciences, in the English-language publication *Soviet Life*, reports that one plant in Kazakhstan is already producing a million and a half gallons of fresh water daily and that a nuclear-powered plant to be built in the same area will produce 350,000 kilowatts of electric power and 27 MGD of fresh water. He, too, indicates the direction desalination is taking when he says, "the capacity of desalting plants must be increased not by just two or three times, but by hundreds of times."

The Role of the Office of Saline Water

Basic research and development of desalination technology in the United States is coordinated by the Office of Saline Water, with a major assist from the Atomic Energy Commission and the active participation of many manufacturers, research and development firms, colleges and universities in the United States and other countries. The OSW has a three-phase program. A short-range phase is aimed at providing the lowest possible desalting costs as soon as possible and applying this technology to areas where natural fresh water is unusually expensive, of poor quality, or in short supply. The intermediate phase is built around the development of advanced technology for use in the 1970's, through experimental pilot-plant operations and the utilization of hardware components. The third phase is directed toward the time beyond 1975 and includes basic research, through which it is hoped new processes and techniques will be found. Under its charter, the OSW is also responsible for providing the technology for purifying such chemically contaminated waters as those into which mine acids drain or irrigation returns flow, in addition to naturally brackish water and sea water. Desalting technology developed under OSW auspices will play an important part in the purification of polluted waters —a world-wide problem.

In the realm of sea-water conversion, desalting plants that can produce water in amounts ranging from less than 1 MGD to over 100 MGD have already been built or are being planned. Most of these are long-tube evaporator or multi-stage flash distillation units, which offer a proven sea-water desalting capability and are economically adaptable to production of fresh water in small or large plant sizes.

For smaller plants, the OSW has developed what might be called a universal 2.5-MGD plant design, for which basic plans—along with specifications and users' manuals—are available. The purpose of this project, according to Dr. Hunter, was "to develop a sound basis for the procurement of high quality plants. . . . The heart of this effort is the development of performance specifications, procedures for procurement, and recommended warranties." The unique engineering package, he said, will "allow a buyer to purchase with confidence on a world-wide basis."

Designed by Burns and Roe, consulting engineers, this package offers eleven different design variations from which local water authorities can choose, and includes a number of procedures for making proper selection to achieve optimum design for widely varied situations. It also includes alternative chemical pretreatment methods for water being desalted at different operating temperatures. When the OSW began developing multistage flash distillation processes, the highest practical temperature to which salt water could be heated was 190° F. before corrosive scale formed by the heated sea water clogged tubes and boilers and reduced operational efficiency. This problem is generic to sea-water conversion and seriously lowered the operating efficiency of early steamships. New techniques in combating scale—a flaky white or rock-hard brownish deposit—with chemical treatment have made it possible to operate distillation plants with temperatures higher than 250° F., and future plants may operate at temperatures as high as 350° F., with greatly improved efficiency and economy. The Clair Engle Plant in San Diego, California, which was dedicated in the late summer of 1967, is designed to operate at that temperature and may be doing so by 1968.

The universal desalting plant package is the first do-it-yourself desalting design kit in engineering history. Its developers provided a set of blueprints that could be used to build an economical water source for any combination of topographic, climatic, inland-water-temperature, and salt-content factors. The 2.5-MGD plant size was selected both for its efficiency and because it is the largest that can be fabricated, transported, and erected without undue problems. Where larger amounts of fresh water are required, the units can be used as modules, operated in tandem and joined only at the fresh-water outlet.

This modular-design approach is increasingly characteristic of large-desalting-plant design. By building such plants in a series of separate units, or modules, which are joined together, water-supply planners can begin producing fresh water without waiting for the entire construction to be completed, can add additional modules if water needs increase without having to redesign and rebuild the entire plant, and can continue to produce at least a reasonable amount of fresh water during periods when one of the modules is closed down for repairs or maintenance. The 150-MGD plant in Los Angeles will be constructed of 50-MGD modules.

In describing the universal package to a meeting of the American Chemical Society, Burns and Roe President Kenneth Roe said, "this is an extremely unusual and exciting concept, which should go far toward alleviating water shortages throughout the world with a minimum of planning time and lower cost."

The concept was inadvertently previewed in 1964, well before the prepackaged "do-it-yourself kit" became available, when a 1-MGD plant near San Diego, California, was dismantled and shipped to Guantanamo Bay, Cuba, by the U.S. Navy. At Guantanamo, it was swiftly reassembled to provide the big American naval base there a guaranteed water supply after Cuban Prime Minister Fidel Castro had ordered the cutting off of pipelines bringing in water from traditional sources.

In addition to the 1-MGD multi-effect, multistage flash distillation plant that began operating in San Diego in the summer of 1967, the OSW also produces 1 MGD of fresh water daily at its Freeport, Texas, test plant, which uses long-tube vertical evaporation processes. This plant is currently experimenting with new tubes that have a heat-transfer coefficient three times that of standard round tubes. They should lead to greater and greater efficiency and, hence, more fresh water for dollars invested and operating costs. It is quite possible, Dr. Hunter suggests, that the long-tube vertical evaporation process may eventually offer better economics than the multistage flash system for large plants because of smaller heat-transfer-surface requirements and reduced pumping costs.

For areas where energy costs for heating salt water are high, industry can now supply solar desalting plants using "greenhouse" stills for widely varied operating conditions. Solar stills can be used in any part of the world where there is enough sunshine. They are inexpensive to construct, but because they require a large area to produce any appreciable amount of fresh water, the capital investment in land may be quite high. A 25,000-gallons-per-day plant would require four to six acres, whereas a flash-distillation plant would require perhaps one-hundredth the land area. Solar stills cost little to operate because the only moving part is a pump. A test plant operated by the OSW in Florida has survived hurricanes without damage. Such stills are used in the Greek islands, parts of Australia (to distill brackish water and provide artificial water holes for cattle), Spain, and Portugal. One plant, providing 6,000 gallons daily, was built in Chile as early as 1875. According to a handbook of solar distillation technology published by the Office of Engineering of the U.S. Agency for International Development (AID), a typical basin-type solar still can be constructed for as little as $720 per thousand square feet (U.S. costs) and 135 man-hours of labor. It requires only asphalt, cement or concrete, glass, piping, trough materials, a pump, and a storage tank. The Mechanical Engineering Division of the Australian Commonwealth Scientific and Industrial Research organization has published do-it-yourself plans for a solar still 130 feet long that will produce 344 gallons daily. Small kits are available also from the University of California.

Although the use of free sunlight energy is attractive, the large capital cost attached to the acreage required for large-scale fresh-water production suggests, says Dr. Hunter, that "whenever any other source of energy is available—waste heat from a diesel electric plant, heat from a process plant, or heat from refuse incineration—it must be seriously considered since this system will usually produce cheaper water on a more reliable schedule."

One solar distillation system, at Puerto Penasco, Mexico, operates around the clock, utilizing storage tanks in conjunction with an evaporator-condenser unit. The sun-heated sea water, which is not used during the day, is fed through the evaporator-condenser unit at night. During the day, normal solar action is used. The resulting fresh water from both processes costs about one-third the price of the brackish water previously trucked in for domestic use. The original system was modified to utilize the waste heat from the cooling jacket and exhaust of a diesel engine, increasing the reliability of the humidification unit, and allowing for continuous daily production of water at a rate of 6,000 gallons. (Some of the social and economic contributions that this one small plant is making are described in other chapters.)

In utilizing waste heat as a low-cost source of thermal energy, the amount of fresh water that can be produced is keyed to the available steam temperatures and pressures, the continuity of waste heat available, the complexity of adapting a steam plant to the source of waste heat, and related factors. It is obvious, however, that desalting plants can in many instances be linked to existing power and industrial plants, which generate heat, but do not use it all.

The OSW is also carrying out a comprehensive program in the engineering development of freezing and hydrate processes. One vacuum-freezing pilot plant at the OSW's Wrightsville Beach, North Carolina, test center, has produced over 100,000 gallons of fresh water daily. An even larger freezing plant has been built in Israel. (Parenthetically, it is interesting that one of the more imaginative schemes suggested for

providing a new source of fresh water is towing gigantic ice-
bergs down from the Arctic regions to the California coast
where they could be melted down.)

Although the oceans offer the largest potential source of
water, there are many inland regions where the only water
source is brackish. These waters have a wide range of contaminants and salinities, some of them more difficult to treat
than salt water. The volume of such waters, available from
rivers, lakes, and underground sources, is such that most inland desalting plants will have capacities below the 10-MGD
level. As indicated earlier, the two most promising means of
demineralizing brackish waters are reverse osmosis and electrodialysis. The former, developed largely by the Office of
Saline Water with major assistance from the University of
California, is being used now in combination with other
treatment methods in sewage and waste-treatment plants such
as those in Santee, California, where reprocessed sewage
comes out purer than the original water that went into the
community's water-supply system.

Reverse-osmosis plants are available in many forms, both
portable and stationary, from American and foreign manufacturers. Some of them consist simply of racks of tubes
packed with membrane through which the water passes; the
individual membranes can be easily replaced if necessary.
The Office of Saline Water has underwritten reverse-osmosis
plants that produce as much as 50,000 gallons of fresh water
daily, and it is currently working on the development of others
to provide as much as 50 MGD. Among the goals of this research and development program are increasing the membrane life from an average of one year to three years and
bringing down the cost of the membranes. The Dupont Company has developed a membrane composed of millions of
fine, hollow fibres, which compresses acres of surface into a
paper-thin membrane and which, as a result, offers considerable economic and engineering advantage. Dow Chemical

Corporation also has a hollow-fiber membrane, which may come into the desalting market place. The OSW alone is funding more than thirty research projects—being carried out in laboratories as widely separated as Alaska and Israel—related to reverse osmosis. Additional research is going on in England, Japan, and other countries. At the International Conference on Water for Peace, Dr. Hunter said that the OSW hoped the first prototype reverse-osmosis plants for municipal use would be feasible sometime in 1969.

Electrodialysis, to date, is used primarily to desalt brackish waters of relatively low salinity. The OSW demonstration plant at Webster, South Dakota, produces a quarter of a million gallons of fresh water daily for that community. Israel has a sizable electrodialysis plant working in the Negev, and there is one providing fresh water for the Kuwait airport. One electrodialysis plant was recently incorporated in the new water-and-sewer system serving the agricultural community of Dell City, Texas, and there are others in the Southwest. The Dell City plant produces 50,000 gallons of high-quality domestic water from plentifully available but gypsum-laden underground water sources.

As noted earlier, a combination of improved membranes, higher-temperature operation, and possible new and basic variations in the electrodialysis process, along with pretreatment to permit its application of what are called "more difficult waters," should lead to reduced operational costs and expand the utilization of this process in water supply. But at present, multistage flash processes dominate the field insofar as small sea-water conversion plants are concerned.

Multistage flash distillation plants in the 1- to 5-MGD capacity, which produce fresh water in the range of 80–90 cents per 1,000 gallons under U.S. conditions, can now be purchased. Further process refinements may eventually lower this figure to 65 cents for 1-MGD plants and even less for larger units, just as it is quite possible that other processes, such as freezing and reverse osmosis, will someday offer lower costs for the smaller plants.

Where larger plants are concerned, much will depend upon the outcome of the development of the first 50-MGD module for the Metropolitan Water District plant in Los Angeles. It is expected that this plant, which will be nuclear-powered and will also provide 1,800 megawatts of electricity for the power grid in the area, will produce water for blending into the MWD system for a cost of about 22 cents per 1,000 gallons.

The U.S.–Mexico Agreement

An ambitious survey being conducted by the United States and Mexico under the general auspices of the International Atomic Energy Agency (IAEA), in accord with an agreement signed in October, 1965, deals with the water needs of parts of the Mexican states of Baja California and Sonora, and Arizona and New Mexico in the United States, and the projected demand for electrical power through 1995 in the area. The states involved have extremely arid, broad valleys, with fertile and highly permeable soil. Currently, parts are irrigated with water from the Colorado River and with underground water. The projected water demands are very large and include rapidly growing municipal and industrial needs and the possibility of vastly expanded farming. The technical and economic feasibility of meeting both water and power requirements with dual-purpose, nuclear-powered desalting plants is a major consideration of the study.

Indeed, the study has been described as the first in which it has been possible to investigate on a real basis the technical practicality and economic potential of extremely large desalting plants. A plant capable of providing a billion gallons of fresh water daily has been chosen as the economic yardstick to be considered. To meet the potential water demand through 1995, several such plants would be required. But

dual-purpose plants of currently accepted design would produce more electrical power than would be absorbed by the
area. Because of this problem, the study will consider special
designs with a high water-to-power ratio, or others intended
for the production of water alone.

One aspect of the study deserves particular mention. Water
from the Gulf of California, where the 1,000-MGD plants
would be located, would have to be transported quite a distance to reach some parts of Arizona, and the cost of transporting water long distances is considerable. However, water
from the Colorado River at Lake Mead, free at the source
insofar as Arizona is concerned, cannot provide substantial
additional supplies for everyone, especially in view of the
steadily increasing demand in Arizona. There isn't enough
water left in the Colorado. Right now, the U.S. Government
is pouring fresh underground water into the lower river to
maintain a lower level of salinity in the water that reaches
Mexico, because the 1944 U.S.–Mexico treaty guarantees
Mexico 1.5 million acre-feet of potable water annually from
the river. The increasing salinity of the Colorado makes it a
dubious long-range source of water unless desalting technology is used by communities and irrigators along its lower
reaches.

The Role of the British

The foregoing has tended to emphasize the work of the
United States in the field of desalination. There is no inten-
tion to downgrade, even by implication, the role the British
have long played in the development and commercial installation of desalting technology. Until recently, one British
firm, Weir Westgarth, could easily claim to have installed
plants with more desalting capacity than any other manufacturer in the world. This may still hold true at the moment,
but the completion of the 2.6-MGD plant at Key West by an

American firm, the building of 7.5-MGD plants by an American firm in Tijuana and a Dutch firm in the Netherlands, both scheduled for completion in 1968, the 5-MGD plant being built by an American firm in Saudi Arabia, and other construction by many firms and by the Soviet Union, may have already, as this is read, changed the statistical leadership. Of the twenty-nine firms listed in the 1966 OSW Annual Report as builders of the various plants existing or planned by January 1, 1967, 5 were British, 15 were American, 1 was West German, 3 Dutch, 1 Israeli, 2 Japanese, 1 Italian, and 1 Swiss. Several of these are branches of international concerns. Still other firms—and the Russians—have since entered the world desalting lists.

The competition for construction contracts is keen, and this is undoubtedly to the benefit of the country or community considering desalting technology in dealing with its water problems. International boundaries, with the possible exception of work within the Soviet Union, seem to have little effect on the nationalities of the firms employed. A Japanese firm installed the OSW electrodialysis plant at Webster, South Dakota. A British firm recently contracted for two plants at Qatar. The Israelis sold a freezing-process plant to Italy. In Kuwait—a country that gets virtually all its water from desalination—British, American, and Japanese manufacturers have built some twenty plants altogether.

It is worth summarizing British activity both to give credit where credit is due and to show how development in the United Kingdom parallels that in the United States.

The commercial history of desalting technology in Great Britain probably began when the firm of G. and J. Weir of Glasgow patented a sea-water evaporator designed to provide boiler-feed water from steam engines on board ships. This was the same firm that, together with Richardson Westgarth, Ltd. (with which it later merged), installed most of the land-based long-tube evaporators in the 1950's. These two firms introduced commercially the multistage flash process, which led to massive increase in unit size and to large-scale cost reduction.

In 1964, the Water Research Association—an organization that performs research projects on behalf of the United Kingdom public water-supply industry—was given a government grant to investigate the part desalting might play in Great Britain's future water resources. The study was still in progress at this writing. In 1965, the United Kingdom Atomic Energy Authority was given responsibility for governmental research in desalting technology. The Authority's initial three-year program has concentrated on multistage flash distillation and how it might be coupled with nuclear power systems and on work on reverse-osmosis and freezing processes.

One interesting new approach to desalting technology for smaller island or coastal communities was introduced by the British at the International Conference on Water for Peace. This was a shipborne desalting plant designed by the United Kingdom Atomic Energy Authority and the British Ship Research Association. Utilizing a multistage flash distillation unit capable of producing 240,000 gallons daily, the desalting ship could visit each of twelve island or coastal communities of about 5,000 population four times a year to pump fresh water into onshore storage facilities. The cost would be about $2.91 per 1,000 gallons, less than many such communities now pay for fresh water brought in by tanker or barge or, if they are coastal, by truck.

(Obviously, comparable units, perhaps of smaller size, could be built on barges and left anchored offshore for periods. One American firm has units that would fit easily onto railroad flatcars, from which they could probably serve a purpose comparable to the desalting ship for communities along a brackish river or a seacoast. Such mobile desalting technology offers a possible water-supply solution for communities too small to afford permanent installations and operation of desalting equipment, especially if there is no immediately obtainable and economical fuel available for its operation.)

Various Applications of the Technology

So far, this chapter has been concerned primarily with technology as technology, and with the nations and firms instrumental in developing it. There are some other points to be made in relationship to the application of desalting technology.

Wherever large-scale plants are discussed, as in the case of Helsinki, Tijuana, Los Angeles, Key West, and the Netherlands, descriptions of the planned installations usually include the word modules. The Burns and Roe package plan talks of adding units by interconnection, as needed.

This modular concept is one of the advantages offered by the new technologies in dealing with water-supply problems, for, as briefly mentioned, it makes possible the planning, installation, and financing of facilities on the basis of both current and projected water needs and the future adequacy and dependability of conventional water resources.

Depending upon the nature of the desalting plant and its energy source, it is quite possible to keep adding modules at appropriate intervals, a relatively simpler process than finding new underground sources, building new reservoirs (where, in the Los Angeles or New York City area, for example, could one find the ground for a new reservoir?), running viaducts for hundreds of miles to other sources (which may have only temporary or short-term value as demand continues to rise over the years), or the building of high-rise dams (which take many years to plan and construct). The addition of modules involves small increments in the amount of land required, as compared to other forms of water supply involving extensive impounding or storage areas.

One very important use of desalination technology is to provide water to blend with existing supplies that have always been or have become too brackish for drinking, for industrial processes, for most irrigation, and for such specialized users as hospitals. This important water-supply function can be the work of both large and small plants. The big 100-MGD plant projected for Israel would provide water for blending into the national water-supply system in that country, to make possible the use of water with marginal or excess salinity. Small plants can not only meet community water needs but also supply water for blending with unsatisfactory existing sources. The capacity of a desalting plant can be designed to be such that when the pure water is added to marginal-quality natural water, the salinity level of the total water would be acceptable for the use desired. Thus, a relatively small desalting plant could make a much larger amount of water usable at a cost much lower than the cost for desalted water alone. At the same time, the below-standard water could still be used for fire-fighting, car washes, and many other purposes not requiring a high level of purity. Such dual-purpose systems exist in some small American and Caribbean Island communities.

There is another way in which desalination plants can serve significantly in providing part of an area's water supply. The British have been studying desalting as a supplementary water source—to be used, basically, to keep water-supply systems at required levels during periods of low flow, low rainfall, or drought. In other words, the desalting plant would be on stand-by a good part of the time, and used only to restore or maintain reservoir or other source levels when they fall during a dry summer or at peak-demand periods, thereby reducing the operating costs of the plant and the capital investment, since a plant could be built on the basis of the amount of the maximum supplemental water needed rather than on the basis of total, day-in-day-out requirements. This supplemental approach would be applicable to the many urban areas where population and industrial development have stabilized because there is no room for additional growth.

On a broader scale, the OSW is studying the utilization of desalting for stand-by supplementation in the drought areas of the northeastern United States. A study made in cooperation with the states of New York and New Jersey and private utility companies in the area sought to determine whether desalination plants could serve to drought-proof the heavily populated and industrialized metropolitan areas of Philadelphia, New Jersey, and New York, which suffer from periodic droughts lasting several years and where present reservoir and ground-water sources cannot meet the demand during subnormal rainfall years without water rationing or other restrictions.

The results of this study, Dr. Hunter reports, indicated that

> . . . appropriately placed desalting plants in the 25 to 50 million gallons per day range would meet the requirement of maintaining minimum levels in existing reservoirs. These plants would only operate about one-third of the time during a weather cycle so they were optimized for low capital costs accepting the resulting higher fuel costs.

The ultimate in such application today is the plant on the island of Guernsey, which, at this writing, had operated less than 5 per cent of the time since its installation in 1960. This plant was installed as protection against drought, so that tomato crops and tourism—bulwarks of Guernsey's traditional economy—would not suffer from water shortages. Considering the cost of drought insurance, the islanders have found the desalting unit a worth-while investment, even though it is inoperative most of the time.

Some Problems To Consider

Certain technical and other problems have to be considered in relation to desalting processes, because they do have a bearing on the over-all considerations water planners have to deal with.

First of all, a desalting plant, regardless of its type, is a mechanical operation and, hence, subject to breakdowns and maintenance requirements. This applies to all the named processes, except perhaps solar distillation, in which a pump is the only working part—and, for it, a period of cloudy days could sharply reduce effectiveness. Desalting plants are subject to total breakdown due to power failures, coastal storms, or major mechanical problems, and, eventually, to a need for replacement.

For several reasons, this is not quite as serious as it sounds. Maintenance, repairs, and replacement are figured into operating costs, and the integration of the plant into a water-supply system can be planned on the basis of "on stream" (the technical term for a plant that is actually producing fresh water) load factors of say 80 or 90 per cent or more. If there is adequate stand-by storage capacity and a good public-education campaign, there is no reason why periodic or occasional outages, when the plant is not functioning or is only partially producing (say, from one module while others are being repaired or maintained), should be any more serious than time lost repairing broken water mains. Certainly, it would usually be less serious than the water-supply time lost after a severe flood or dam break has disrupted conventional municipal water supplies. Although it would be expected that most plant operators would stock some basic replacement parts, manufacturers today insist that most of the key parts—tubes, boilers, membranes—could be replaced by prefabricated units. After Hurricane Carla in 1961, when this writer first saw the OSW's Freeport plant, it was almost completely under salt water. But it was repaired and back on stream in less than a week.

In 1966, Kaiser Engineers undertook to study the problem of desalting plant breakdowns in connection with the 150-MGD plant planned for the Metropolitan Water District of Southern California and the 100-MGD plant projected for the Government of Israel. The study was sponsored by the MWD, Israel, the Office of Saline Water, and the Atomic Energy Commission and was made by N. Arad, representing the Joint Seawater Desalting Project, Israel; S. F. Mulford, Manager of the OSW San Diego Seawater Test Facility; and J. R. Wilson, Manager of Desalting Engineering Development for Kaiser.

Their analysis was based on assumptions that the plants would consist of four basic desalting units, with each evaporator producing its designed-for capacity when operating; that the availability of steam from the adjacent nuclear power plants would be 90 per cent; that scheduled shutdowns for maintenance would be performed during scheduled shutdowns for adjacent steam power plants; that outages due to fouling of intake facilities by marine hazards such as fish, dumped oil, and other pollutants and drifting objects would affect the power-plant availability rather than the desalting operation itself; that salinity level would not exceed 125 PPM of total dissolved solids (based on a production level of 25 PPM, permitting a rise of 100 PPM due to leaks before the plant must be shut down for repairs); that bugs would have been taken out of the plants, and all initial failures due to faulty materials, manufacture, or assembly would have been corrected; and that failures of any one component that might force the plant to shut down would not occur simultaneously with failures occurring in other components.

This study concluded that "the results obtained do indicate that the 94 per cent mean desalting plant availability or, equivalently, the 95 per cent dual purpose mean plant operating factor assumed in some recent studies is not unreasonable." One interesting detail is the projection that probable failure of the thousands of miles of tubing in the large plants would be only 1,200 out of 940,000 tubes in the thirtieth year of operation, when such failures would be at their maximum.

The use of nickel alloy and titanium tubing and improved chemical treatments of the water have apparently reduced the problem of corrosion and scale to easily manageable levels. Research in this field will undoubtedly continue. One firm is now producing aluminum units, weighing and costing less, for the U.S. Army, indicating that corrosion problems related to this less costly metal are well on their way to being solved.

There is still, however, the difficulty of what besides salt water goes into a desalting plant. In reviewing plant location and projected plant efficiency, one important factor is the location of the intake openings in relation to sewage, pollutants, fish, and other things that may be found in the water to be desalted. Oil in the water is one such problem. Often, it may be preferable to put the plant on a brackish estuary in from the coast, where intake systems are as far away as possible from oil loading or unloading docks, to avoid the steady increase of oil contamination. Although oil generally floats near or on the surface, the massive suction of a plant taking in millions of gallons of water might well bring some of the sludge or waste oil into the desalting system. (Curiously, oil companies are now using some desalting processes to remove water from crude oil.) The new Key West desalting plant uses intake wells sunk below the ocean bottom, thereby minimizing the problem of solids and fish in the sea water.

Plant efficiency will also relate to the degree of salinity and other mineralization involved. The Red Sea, and some other seas, are saltier than the oceans. The Gulf of Aqaba, where Baldwin-Lima-Hamilton built a desalting plant for the Israeli port of Eilat, contained an extremely large amount of Epsom salts, which was taken out of the water along with the other salts, to the temporary discomfiture of the residents.

Another problem is the taste of the water. As anyone who has ever boiled water knows, distilled water is flat and tasteless. People don't like it. As a result, most of the newer plants supplying fresh water for human consumption treat it by passing it through limestone or with another process to put some taste back into it.

Coastal plants have the problem of treating and cooling effluent brine before putting it back into the ocean. There is considerable controversy over the effect heated waste water has on marine life when it is dumped back into a bay, ocean, or river. Heating removes the oxygen from the water, and this affects the water quality by destroying or diminishing some of the bacteria that break down solid wastes, and by encouraging the growth of harmful algae—which, in turn, remove what oxygen is left. Heating has a definitely harmful effect on shellfish and some other forms of marine life. In the Los Angeles area, some people anticipate that the outflow of warm brine will actually improve tuna-breeding off the coast of southern California, but others say that if this happens, then more sharks will come dangerously close to shore to feed off the young tuna. Such arguments may be colorful, but the problem is there, and it needs to be considered when a plant is constructed, so that warm brine can either be cooled sufficiently or piped far enough out to sea or up the coast to minimize any bad effects.

A much more serious problem affects inland plants desalting brackish water. What do you do with the salt?

According to Dr. Wilburn G. Schroeder of the University of Maryland, a chemical engineer who is familiar with desalination problems, a brackish-water desalting plant producing 10 MGD of fresh water would have an intake volume of 18 MGD. Assuming a brackishness level of 9,000 PPM of dissolved salts, this plant would produce 400 tons of solids daily, or 134,000 tons per year, in the form of hot brine, moving probably into evaporation lagoons. Such lagoons must be lined and treated to prevent the concentrated saline or mineralized water from leaking into the ground and further mineralizing ground waters and, eventually, nearby streams and rivers.

In terms of dry-salt quantities, the plant Dr. Schroeder described would produce twenty-five acres of salt, one foot deep, each year.

One can easily conjure up visions of vast salt piles spread across the land. They would be whiter versions of the slag heaps that disfigure the countryside around mining towns. How much of this salt can be used commercially no one has estimated, but undoubtedly it will be nowhere near the amount involved, especially if salt begins to pile up in many places. One suggestion is to bury it, another to pump the brine underground. Both have several obvious disadvantages. Remove it? Are there enough trucks and railroad cars available? And where will you take it?

At present, there are no inland plants producing anything close to 10 MGD of fresh water. By the time they are needed, some solution to this problem will have to be developed—perhaps something similar to experiments now under way, in which refuse from large cities is being transported to areas where it is used to fill in abandoned coal mines, so that the surface land can be restored. It is a problem some water-supply people joke about—or offer as a reason why desalination is not a practical answer to the world's needs.

It is a problem that stands between a community and its future water supply. It is one that must be solved, and well before too much salt piles up.

One other problem should be mentioned, at least in passing. Desalting is only one part of a community's, a region's, or a nation's water management plan. In designing such plans, full consideration must be given to the total plan, so that the community doesn't suddenly find itself with a source of water and no place to put it. Concurrent with the building of the desalting plant, appropriate pipelines and pumping stations to move the water into existing distribution systems or storage facilities, which, if they do not exist, should also be built, and considerably prior to the day the new desalting plant goes on stream.

If desalting technology is to help meet human needs and to improve the living standards of a community or country—for better drinking water, faster fire-fighting, for industry, for agriculture—it has to be used in conjunction with total planning and total investment in construction of water systems.

How this is being done today in many countries will be discussed in the following chapter. Succeeding chapters will treat specific applications of the new desalting technology to agriculture, industry, and developing nations.

2

For Man the Inhabitant

"Water development can be a very helpful instrument in achieving social and economic objectives. . . . It is admirably adapted to planning for 'man the inhabitant.' "

These simple but striking statements made by Edward A. Ackerman, Executive Officer of the Carnegie Institution, at the International Conference on Water for Peace, provide a basic perspective from which to view the role that desalination is and will be playing in mankind's struggle to survive— a struggle modern, industrialized society faces alongside the so-called backward nations.

The Honorable Carlos P. Romulo, Secretary of Education for the Philippines, speaks for the underdeveloped countries of the world when he says, "Year after year, the challenge of water poses problems to our peoples at the most elemental level of challenges to man—i.e., at the precarious level of survival." Dr. Charles C. Bradley, Dean of the College of Letters and Science at Montana State University, is one who speaks for the United States, saying that, if we do not develop new water resources or find better ways of using those that do exist, "young Americans alive today will see a significant deterioration in their standard of living before they are much past middle age."

It is estimated that the number of inhabitants on earth will be doubled by the end of this century and will continue increasing until it reaches perhaps 20 billion in the middle of the twenty-first century. This will bring steadily increasing— in fact, drastically increasing—needs for water to grow the food required to feed the billions of new inhabitants, to supply the homes in which they will live, to make possible the industrial processes that will provide jobs for most of them. With a generally, although erratically, improving standard of living in many countries, per-capita water use will increase, particularly among exploding urban and suburban populations. With parallel increases in industrial and agricultural water use, the noted planner and water expert, Constantinos Doxiadis, predicts that per-capita water needs will double by the year 2,000 and will probably level off a century later without reaching a level three times that of today's per-capita water usage.

Within this context of population and water use, he suggests that "total consumption of water will be five times greater for the year 2000 and fifteen times greater a hundred years from now," and that, to meet this phenomenally growing water demand, "man will have to change his attitude toward the collection and use of water . . . he will have to search for new sources, try to re-use the polluted water, desalinate the sea water and control much greater quantities of the rainfall which is now wasted in the oceans."

Professor Doxiadis is just one of many experts who look to desalting technology as part of the solution to world water-supply problems. Richard L. Meier, a well-known demographer from the University of Michigan, told a world population symposium at Georgetown University that future cities must be able to reprocess and desalt water if they are to survive. And Lewis Mumford, the famed commentator on metropolitan affairs, wrote in *The City in History* that large cities are running out of available water as they spread out, destroying or filling in local supply sources while at the same time demanding more and more water for their burgeoning populations, air-conditioning systems, and industries. The only solution he can see for "this chronic shortage of water in metropolitan agglomerations" is "the distillation of sea water in wholesale quantities."

From the Canary Islands to the Caspian Sea

Recognition of the potential for desalination is world-wide.

In 1965, Spanish representatives at the First International Symposium on Water Desalination reported that projected building of thermal power plants in many parts of Spain and its possessions offered "interesting possibilities for the simultaneous production" of both power and water through dual-purpose plants, especially in chronically water-short regions in southeastern Spain. They cited the special cases of Ceuta in Spanish Morocco and the cities of Arrecife, Lanzarote, and Las Palmas de Gran Canaria in the Canary Islands, where such dual-purpose plants have been built to supply both water and power, because water reserves were virtually exhausted. In Ceuta, two plants of 1-MGD capacity were constructed by a West German firm. The plants in the Canary Islands are being built by American and Dutch manufacturers and will have a combined capacity of more than 5.2 MGD of fresh water.

In the Netherlands, where ground-water resources are barely sufficient to cover current water needs, and the Rhine, a major source of water, has become too polluted or mineralized for normal use, work has begun on a 7.5-MGD desalination plant that will make fresh water from tidal salt water in the West Schelde estuary of the Schelde River, near Neuzen. The plant, which will be operated in conjunction with an electric power station, will cost about $10 million and is part of a desalination program being developed in anticipation of a tripled demand for water by the year 2000.

At the International Conference on Water for Peace, K. C. Zijlstra, Director of the Netherlands Government Institute of Sewage Purification and Industrial Waste Treatment, reported an alarming increase in pollution and salinity of the Rhine as it passes through Holland. This increase is particularly critical to the Dutch because, as he said, the Rhine contributes about 65 per cent of the nation's fresh-water supply. The salinization, which has risen markedly since World War II, comes not only from human wastes but also from potassium mines in Alsace, coal mines in the Ruhr, Emscher, and Lippe districts, and from the soda industry. Director Zijlstra said that "in times of low flow, the concentration is rising toward a value that exceeds the international drinking-water standards and also causes detrimental effects to agriculture and horticulture."

Expensive antipollution measures, including the use of desalting technology, will be required if the Rhine is to continue to provide usable fresh water for the Dutch. Prior to beginning work on the big plant near Neuzen, the Dutch built an experimental fresh-water desalter at the site of the Royal Dutch Blast Furnaces and Steelworks at Ymuiden, where the steel-mill power plant provided the steam needed for the desalting unit. This plant, which produced better than 200,000 gallons of fresh water daily, is being shipped to the island of St. Martin in the Netherlands Antilles to provide drinking water there.

There are many dramatic examples of how desalting is or shortly will be contributing to the well-being of communities whose population and living standards were declining or whose growth and development were stymied by existing or potential water problems.

Hundreds of islands in the Greek archipelago are completely arid and depend upon rain for their natural water supply. The rains are collected from roofs during the winter and stored in cisterns for household use during the rest of the year. Most houses have individual cisterns, and on some islands there are community reservoirs. Those few islands that can afford it obtain water from a commercial service, which tows supplies in plastic containers at a cost of $3.00 per 1,000 gallons. When the cisterns on other islands run dry, the Greek Government uses funds allocated for water-shortage emergencies to send tankers. Although the islanders are not charged for this water, the cost to the Greek Government is even higher than the $3.00 figure.

For some of the islands, this pattern of limited supply and recurrent emergency has been reversed by the use of solar distillation to make fresh water from the sea or from brackish water on the islands. The stills capitalize on the fact that the sun shines for about 300 days per year, and the low humidity and high sunlight radiation values that make the Greek islands ideal places for solar conversion of sea water.

The first of these solar desalting units was installed on the Dodecanese island of Symi in 1964. It was one of four desalting units provided to Greek islanders by the Church World Service and paid for by an anonymous American donor who had heard of the islanders' water plight. A Minnesota firm did the construction. In addition to the plant on Symi, one was built on the roof of the YMCA camp on the island of Salamis, a third in the community of Perdika, on Aegina, and a fourth on Santorin.

What has desalted fresh water meant to the islanders—people so poor their communities could not afford the price of the relatively cheap construction involved, could not, in some cases, provide the electricity to run the pumps?

On Symi, where the cisterns used to run dry in July and remain dry until the rains came in October and November, people left the island during the summer—and tourists stayed

away. Often, some of the islanders did not return. This movement away from Symi has slowed down now that water is
available the year round, and the incidence of dysentery has
dropped from an average of 300 cases a year to perhaps one
or two. The town square is occupied in part by the solar still
and has literally become a focal point of life on the island in
more ways than one.

On Aegina, where people who did not have cisterns in
which to store rainfall traveled three to five miles for water,
which was often brackish, Wilson Radway, Special Projects
Director of the Church World Service, reports a vast improvement in the food prepared by island housewives, who said,
among other things, that the cooking time for beans had been
cut to less than half by the utilization of distilled water.

The Greek Ministry of Industry has also initiated a solar
distillation program for the islanders, hoping eventually to
free all of them from dependence on rain water. In 1965,
four solar desalting stills were built on Kímolos, Nisyros,
Patmos, and on the roof of a hotel in Symi.

As elsewhere, the Greek Islands' solar stills also catch some
rain, thereby increasing their yield of potable water. To see
if the program can be otherwise expanded, the Technical
University at Athens has built a Solar Experiment Station on
Symi to provide research support for this water-supply program.

In 1967, Dr. A. Delyannis and Dr. E. Piperglou of the
Technical University discussed the Patmos still at the Second
European Symposium on Fresh Water from the Sea. They
described Patmos as a community where development was
hindered by insufficient water resources and by inadequate
sanitary conditions for the collection of what was available.
The lower part of the town had a piping system to which
some houses and public water tubs were connected. In the
upper part of town, water supply was dependent on rain
water caught and stored in individual cisterns. In wintertime,

rain water was also collected from a nearby ravine and stored in five small reservoirs with a total capacity of about 500,000 gallons. Some additional well water was pumped, untreated, into the reservoirs in summertime. In years of low rainfall, the situation became critical and water was consumed with "great caution and only for strictly indispensable purposes," they reported. If the shortage became acute, the government had to ship in water by tanker. Under almost every circumstance, "water consumption per capita was considered to be excessively low."

When it was decided to build the solar still at Patmos, there was broad participation in the project. The Council of St. John's Abbey in Patmos donated the land; the Greek Government provided funds for construction; Dr. Delyannis and Dr. Piperglou contributed technical advice and drawings; the Hellenic Industrial Development Bank took the erection of the plant as a nonprofit project. All the people of Patmos had to pay for was operation and maintenance. Today, the Patmos still provides about 7,000 gallons of water daily.

Greece, incidentally, has not limited its desalination work to solar distillation. Recently, the city of Phoenix, in Crete, asked bids on construction of a plant that would produce between 395,000 to 530,000 gallons daily. In March, 1967, a team of Greek and U.S. specialists completed a feasibility study to see whether desalination could economically supplement the water supply for the city of Athens. A nuclear-powered plant producing 50 MGD along with electric power was recommended and its 33-cents-per-1,000-gallons cost is now being compared with other water-resource possibilities.

The Key West story is dramatic in a different way. Let the Associated Press introduce it:

> Key West, Florida, (AP)—in the third month of a searing drought, Key West faced a crisis. Water reserves were dangerously low, and its 56,000 residents were on severe rations. The city was tense because a fire could mean catastrophe.

Then from the sea that surrounds it, millions of gallons of pure water gushed into the city's mains. And suddenly long years of shortages brought by drought and hurricane were gone forever.

Key West had turned to the sea, mightiest of reservoirs, to solve a problem that has plagued peoples of many lands through all of recorded history.

A desalting plant has just gone into operation. It sucks up five million to six million gallons of sea water a day and sends it coursing through a maze of superheated pipes and chambers. Then, out one end pour 2,620,000 gallons of water so pure it must be cascaded over a bed of lime to give it body and taste. From the other end, mineral-laden residue flows back to the sea.

Key West, a coral island at the southern end of the Florida Keys, has no fresh-water streams of any kind. Until 1941, it relied for fresh water on rains caught and stored in cisterns. Then the U.S. Navy built a pipeline to carry 6 MGD of water from Florida City on the mainland to its big Key West base. Half of this water was sold to the community for domestic use. Hurricanes were one problem. For example, in 1960 Hurricane Donna broke the pipeline as it also destroyed bridges and communications lines in the Keys. Then, in 1962, the naval base was enlarged after the Cuban missile crisis. Key West's population had already grown since 1941, and the number of tourists coming down for vacation visits was increasing steadily. There wasn't enough water to go around.

Originally, the Florida Keys Aqueduct Commission planned to build another pipeline with a capacity that would not be fully used until 1990. It would have cost $40 million. The salt-water conversion plant cost only $3.37 million—less than one-tenth the cost of the proposed aqueduct.

The desalting plant is now producing fresh water for 85 cents per 1,000 gallons, which is a bargain for water-short Key West. The community is already planning to build a second desalination plant of comparable size to guarantee water for future use. In the meantime, Key West is free of its water famine and does not have to worry about hurricane breaks in the pipeline, or drought.

The Key West drought, incidentally, points up the total Florida water problem. Although the state is largely a peninsula bordered by the Gulf of Mexico and the Atlantic Ocean, it is subject to periodic droughts. Northern and central Florida draw underground water from limestone beds reaching back up into Alabama and Georgia. In 1967, winter and spring rains were relatively light; the underground water source was sparse—so sparse, in fact, that in some places the waterless subterranean limestone structure collapsed, taking houses down into unexpected sinkholes. Water was rationed in many parts of the state. In southern Florida, the largest surface-water source is Lake Okeechobee; so much water has been diverted from the lake to meet domestic needs that the famed Florida Everglades, one of the United States' greatest wildlife preserves, has begun to dry up for want of water from Lake Okeechobee.

Yet, paradoxically, there is not a populous community in Florida that is any great distance from the ocean or the Gulf of Mexico. Certainly, today's desalination technology could at the very least provide the state with supplementary water to augment underground or other sources in times of drought. With its population and agriculture—it is the second largest cattle-raising state in America and a major producer of citrus fruits—growing steadily, Florida would seem to be a natural place for desalting to take hold.

Across the continent, Aqua-Chem, Inc. is building a 7.6-MGD desalting plant for the Mexican city of Tijuana, just below the border between Mexico and the United States. Tijuana is a seacoast community where the water has long been unsatisfactory, but tolerated. A large part of Tijuana's economy is based on tourism. Americans flock across the border to enjoy bullfights and night life, and to shop for souvenirs. One-day or overnight tourists put up with water that tastes poor, but Tijuana is interested in more substantial tourism and over-all community growth. The population today is close to 300,000, but it is expected to reach a half a million by 1970 and perhaps a million before the end of the decade following.

In hope of achieving a new image and becoming more than a honky-tonk tourist attraction, Tijuana is improving public services such as street repair, garbage collection, and police and fire protection. Individual Tijuanans, stimulated by a new-found sense of civic pride and interest, have contributed $160,000 of their own money to the public-works program. There is federal support, too, for Tijuana's emergence as an important city in northern Mexico. The Mexican Government is financing the desalination plant, which will operate in conjunction with an already operating electric power plant at Rosarito. A fourth unit is being added to the plant, to make it the largest of its kind in Mexico, with a 300,000-kilowatt capacity. The state government of Baja California has agreed to finance the distribution system for the water from the desalting plant, at a cost of $16 million. Before deciding in favor of desalination, Mexican authorities compared the costs of desalting with those of an aqueduct system that would have brought water from nearby Mexicali to augment the present water supply from the Tijuana River and wells, inadequate both as to quantity and quality.

It is obvious, as one reads about the Dodecanese, Key West, and Tijuana, that desalination is becoming more and more important in the world water picture. It is not the purpose of this chapter, however, to do a country-by-country study of how the technology is or is not being used, but only to pick some examples for illustrative purposes. Israel and Saudi Arabia provide perhaps the most important examples of the role of desalting in social and economic development, the former because it looks to desalting to perpetuate development when all other water resources are used, and the latter because it keys desalting to a nation-wide effort to improve living standards and stabilize the nomadic population. The experience of both these countries will be discussed at greater length in Chapter VI.

Certain other countries and situations illustrate more directly the relationship of desalting to man the inhabitant, and his social development.

Italy is one nation in which a steady increase in population and rapid industrial growth has drawn attention to an urgent need for better utilization and preservation of traditional natural water resources and. for the development of artificial sources. Whole regions, such as southern Italy, are looking to desalination to help make possible industrial expansion, which is tied to the availability of fresh water for the processes involved and for the workers and their families.

Basic work in this field has been assigned to Italy's National Research Council, which in 1966 began a special study of desalination processes. Participating also are the Hydrographic Service of the Ministry of Public Works, the Fund for the Development of the South, the National Nuclear Energy Committee, and the Ministry of Health. The National Research Council in May, 1967, opened a test and research station at Bari, on the Adriatic Sea, which is comparable to the OSW Research Center at Wrightsville Beach. A steel plant complex in southern Italy has installed a 1.2-MGD plant to bring in fresh water from a brackish inland source, and a freezing-process plant capable of producing 100,000 gallons of fresh water daily has been purchased from Israel. Once this plant has been tested at Bari, it will probably be moved to one of the arid southern island areas. Several solar stills have been completed for isolated coastal towns.

Southern Italy and its islands are much like the Greek islands. The smaller locations are supplied by tank ships or from whatever rainfall they can catch and store, but the increasing water demand has made such sources inadequate. The first ten desalting plants built under the new program will be in this part of Italy.

Italy's water needs will increase by more than 50 per cent by the year 2015, according to the Department of Public Works. Accordingly, says Dr. Roberto Passino of the National Research Council, "for what concerns Italy, desalination will be a tool of social and economic progress."

The Soviet Union has also shown great interest in desalting, as was indicated earlier. A nuclear-powered desalting plant is being built at Fort Shevchenko on the Mangyshlak Peninsula. It is already producing over 1 MGD for a new industrial city on the Caspian Sea and will be expanded to many times that capacity as the city grows. A 125-MGD plant is also planned for the Caspian area, but this involves the redirection of river flows to restore the Caspian to its former level. This sea, like the Great Lakes in the United States, has been losing depth as more and more water is taken from it or the rivers that feed it.

One Soviet scientist, quoted by the Novosti Press Agency, talks of desalination with great urgency when he says, "Drastic action should be taken immediately to put the water economy in good order and develop desalting procedures. Otherwise, many parts of the country will be threatened with a water famine in five or ten years."

India's "Gamble in Rains"

India is a country desperately in need of additional water resources, yet its approach to desalination is extremely cautious.

Dr. D. R. Anand, Minister of Water and Electricity, predicts that desalting processes will be used for industry first, then for large urban areas, and will "undoubtedly be a major resource" by the year 2000, when the cost of desalted water comes down and the population of his country is way, way up. There is some discussion of using desalination to help solve water problems for the big cities, and reports to the Second European Symposium on Fresh Water from the Sea in May, 1967 indicated that research is being conducted in the application of solar distillation in small isolated coastal communities with no other resources.

"Our budget is a gamble in rains," G. L. Mehta, one of India's top investment authorities and former Ambassador to the United States, told a financial reporter for *The New York Times* in a story that appeared on July 16, 1967. He added, "The rains have come to 11 of our 17 districts. If the rains continue and spread to the rest of the country it will be a big boost to our efforts to accelerate economic growth. Evenly distributed, the rains will help us lower the price of food grains. If we hold food prices we can hold the economy."

A month earlier, the *Times* correspondent in New Delhi, Joseph Lelyveld, had reported:

India has watched the majestic advance of the rains this year with even more anxiety than usual, for the last two monsoons were anything but kind, leaving large patches of drought and calamity. For months, Cabinet ministers and landless laborers have shared a common refrain, "If only the rains are good."

Between now and September, when the monsoon begins its slow retreat from the subcontinent, the country will receive nearly 90 percent of its total annual rainfall. Thus what happens in the early days of the rainy season is only a portent.

Last year in Bihar, the rains began excellently. Then midway through the season they stopped, never to resume. Crops that had been well-sown perished in the fields before they could be harvested.

The Bihar story has been well documented. Tank trucks rushed water to small farm communities. Hand drills were widely distributed to help Indian farmers try to wrest some ground water from the soil. Only by dint of massive effort and imports of grain and some crop successes elsewhere was India able to escape the threat of mass death from hunger.

At present, Indian farmers in most areas grow one crop a year, when they get enough (not too much, not too little) rain from the monsoons. With a guaranteed source of water and modern farming techniques, they could grow two or even three crops—something Saudi Arabia, with only occasional, disastrous monsoon rains in a tiny part of its whole area, is trying to achieve with the help of desalination as part of its total water planning. Under existing circumstances, a farmer could only earn 25 cents for rice grown with 32 cents worth of desalted water. However, even if this price differential continued in the face of improved farming, desalting might well be worth the investment if the new source of water brought two or three crops year round to the farmer, increasing his income and making him a stronger part of the consumer economy. It would also save the money now spent on purchase and transportation of grains elsewhere and the large investment in what seem to be perpetual emergency measures. With a bigger income, the farmer could become a more important consumer and source of tax revenues.

Although India's interest in desalination at present does not include broad agricultural use of desalted water, the country is studying the possibilities of the technology as a source of water for at least two of its large cities. The feasibility of desalting plants for Madras and Bombay was studied by the Atomic Energy Establishment, which reported the lowest possible cost for fresh water from a dual-purpose, nuclear-powered desalting operation would be more than twice the water rate paid in other Indian cities. Work continues at various national laboratories in India, but the nation's high power and fuel costs and huge unused water resources seem to be limiting the scope of desalination to remote places, where relatively small amounts of water are required and high water costs are traditional. Whether India will find that the cost of mining untapped ground waters and transporting them by pipeline is more expensive than desalting—as witness Key West—remains to be seen.

Shortages in England, Japan, and Finland

From monsoon Asia to misty England seems a long jump, but Great Britain also has population problems, which, in turn, have created water problems.

In 1965, the First International Symposium on Water Desalination heard reports of severe local water shortages in the United Kingdom. Although about 96 billion gallons of rain fall on England and Wales daily, and 50 billion could be made available for use, less than one-eighth of the latter amount is actually caught for use. What's more, the areas of high rainfall are in the northwestern part of the British Isles and the centers of population are concentrated in the southeast. The cost of transporting water from any newly found water sources would be high, and there is little, if any, room for new reservoirs in the populated areas. The Water Resources Board, formed in 1964, is considering two main alternatives for increasing the water supplies: damming up river estuaries to form reservoirs, and desalting the seas that surround England.

In other parts of the world, large cities such as Yokohama and Helsinki are also looking into desalination to supply the water they need for the future.

The Kanagawa Prefecture of Japan, which includes the city of Yokohama, expects to reach a population of 6 million by 1975, a 33 per cent increase in just ten years. The Prefecture has been in the water-planning business for thirty years, but is running out of new sources to tap. In May, 1967, the Prefecture reported that "the only conceivable method capable of supplying a stabilized yet large amount of water of good quality . . . is desalination of sea water." The report noted that costs of conventional river-water resources were rising steadily, while the cost of desalted water was dropping. But whether or not the desalted water cost actually reaches that of river water, the Prefecture is determined to achieve desalination capability as soon as possible, "to secure a stabilized and eternal source of water supply for the residents of Kanagawa."

Paradoxically, the use of desalted water in Japan started as a by-product of salt production. By late 1965, there were three salt factories providing fresh water for domestic use. The Mitsubishi-Sakito salt factory in the Nagasaki Prefecture pipes over 525,000 gallons of residual fresh water daily to a reservoir, where it is mixed with pond water and ultimately fed into a city water system. Two other factories, in the Kanagawa and Hiroshima prefectures, supply lesser amounts.

Two years before the Yokohama water planners announced their plans for using desalination, Masso Hashizumo, representing Japan at the First International Symposium on Water Desalination, virtually predicted their conclusions. He said the demand for water, especially in densely populated coastal areas, was exceeding the supply no matter what conservation steps were taken, and that to make up the growing deficits with desalting technology would increase the water rates by only one yen per capita for an average day. (This comes to one American dollar per man per year.)

In Finland, a committee headed by Eino Kajaste, managing director of the Helsinki Waterworks, has recommended that the city consider desalting water from the Gulf of Finland, an arm of the Baltic Sea, to augment fresh water now coming from Lake Hiidenvesi and the Vantaa River. The currently used sources will be inadequate by 1980, the committee said, and recommended that an initial module with a capacity of 13.8 MGD be built about fifteen kilometers east of Helsinki, next to a proposed nuclear power plant, and that additional modules be added until the total reaches 115 MGD by 1990.

Communities on the fringes of coastal deserts, which comprise 19 per cent of the total land surface of the earth, may also be prime candidates for applied desalination, which could bring them new vitality and commercial development and raise their living standards. These will be discussed in more detail in later chapters.

Desalting in the United States

With the possible exception of Kuwait, which gets almost all of its water from desalination plants, the United States seems, at this writing, to be doing more with the application of desalting technology than any other nation.

Key West now gets its water from desalting. Catalina Island, forty miles off the coast of Los Angeles, has been using a sea-water desalting plant since 1965 to supplement inadequate supplies made even shorter by the weekend tourist influx. In San Diego, California, a new 1-MGD sea-water desalting plant has been built for the Office of Saline Water. Water from desalting is being used in the municipal water systems in Coalinga, California; Webster, South Dakota; Freeport, Texas; and Buckeye, Arizona. Dell City, Texas, recently ordered a desalination plant as part of its municipal water-supply and sewage system, and Port Mansfield, Texas, also has purchased a desalting plant. A recent survey by the Southwest Research Institute of Texas recommended eleven cities as communities that could economically use desalination plants. Another study is investigating the possibility of providing fresh water from the Gulf of Mexico for nine cities close to Brownsville, Texas.

In the Virgin Islands, desalination has become a major source of water supply and will be even more so as both the permanent and tourist populations grow. St. Thomas, the largest of the islands, was paying about $2.00 per 1,000 gallons for water, most of which came by barge from Puerto Rico. Westinghouse recently completed a desalting plant on St. Thomas to produce 1 million gallons of water and 7,500 kilowatts of electricity. The water costs will be less than half of what the islanders formerly paid. The same firm also built a 1.5-MGD desalination plant on the island of St. Croix, where another desalting plant, to produce 2.5 MGD of fresh water is under construction and an additional 1-MGD plant will also be built.

The state of New York is planning to build an experimental 1-MGD plant near Riverhead, Long Island, and there are those who see desalting as the best answer to water problems on Long Island. This 110-mile-long island has a population of 2 million (outside New York City limits), a declining, increasingly polluted underground water supply, and problems with sea-salt incursions on the water table. Yet, like Florida, it is bounded in large measure by salt water. Its steady growth in terms of population and industry would make it a natural beneficiary from desalination, the cost of which could probably be borne without too much pain by the residents through their tax or water bills.

However, although the Metropolitan Water District of Southern California, among others, has found valid reasons for expending a large amount of money to obtain fresh water from the ocean for a large metropolitan area, not all water experts agree that this necessarily makes sense at this time.

Abel Wolman, an internationally recognized water authority from Johns Hopkins University and water adviser to New York City, maintains that the Hudson River is a better source of water for New York City than desalting plants. He feels it is cheaper to bring water from the St. Lawrence River, a distance of 270 miles, or Lake Champlain, also more than 200 miles, or the upper watershed of the Susquehanna, than it would be to build and operate desalination units.

In a recently published statement, he notes that New York gets its water delivered by gravity flow for only about 15 cents per 1,000 gallons and that "the lowest predicted cost for desalination, assuming a plant with a capacity of 250 million or more gallons, is a highly optimistic 30 to 50 cents per thousand gallons." He adds further that the cost of pumping the water from a sea-level desalting plant to higher elevations and transporting it to the users would add about 20 cents per 1,000 gallons.

It would seem that Dr. Wolman's statement must have been prepared prior to the completion and publication of the Southern California study, which not only projects a 22-cents-per-1,000-gallons cost for desalted water for Los Angeles but also indicates that water can be transported for an additional 5 cents per 1,000 gallons to a mixing station 26 miles from and 810 feet higher than the new plant to be built on Bolsa Chica Island. If, as suggested by the recent OSW study for New York and New Jersey, smaller plants were to be built to supplement the New York reservoir system during low-flow or drought periods, Dr. Wolman's analysis would not necessarily hold true. Also, New York City might not have to pump water as far and as high as Los Angeles expects to. What's more, the most recent estimates of New York City's water costs in the immediate future under the present system have risen to 20 cents per 1,000 gallons.

As this is being written, however, New York City water planners, watching the California developments, are considering the possibilities of desalting as a factor in the future of the city's water supply. In Mid-1968, the Atomic Energy Commission and the Consolidated Edison Company of New York began studying the use of man-made islands or other locations for dual-purpose plants to meet the future demands for power and water. In commenting on the new studies, Consolidated Edison Chairman Charles F. Luce noted that the city's Board of Water Supply was considering desalting but was not optimistic about desalted water's becoming economically competitive with other sources. "I wish I could tell you that desalting will be competitive, or rather when it will be competitive, for I have little doubt that nuclear desalting one day will be an important part of the answer to our fresh water supply problems," he told the forum, "Nuclear Energy and Man's Need for Water."

California is the only state in the United States with a comprehensive water plan, adopted by the state legislature in 1957. As part of this plan, a new 700-mile aqueduct, which will cross two mountain chains, is bringing water from the Feather River into southern California, and there are still other resources further north to tap—if necessary and if a growing population doesn't use it there first. At present, the water problems are largely in the southern part of the 1,000-mile-long state. There, tremendous population booms and agricultural and industrial development have created an enormously increased demand for water. The Metropolitan Water District, which includes Los Angeles and several other communities, has been getting its water from a variety of sources, including the Colorado River, the Owens River, and various mountain and underground sources. By 1971 or 1972, it will be entitled to over 2 million acre-feet annually from the Feather River aqueduct, almost twice what its Colorado River aqueduct now delivers to the MWD communities on the coastal plains of southern California.

In spite of these resources, which appear sufficient for the near future, on August 9, 1966, the Board of Directors of the Metropolitan Water District reached a decision that is a landmark in the history of desalination. This was a decision to go ahead with the design and construction of a combination nuclear power and desalting plant in collaboration with the U.S. Government and private electric power companies in southern California. It will be the largest such plant in the world.

The Metropolitan Water District's interest in desalting dates back to the late 1950's, when a preliminary study was submitted to the board of directors. No action was taken until 1963, when the board felt that possible plant sites were getting scarce, so it would be well to look at the question again and perhaps take action to acquire the land. It then signed a contract with the Office of Saline Water and the Atomic Energy Commission for a study of the venture to determine its engineering and economic feasibility. This study was carried out by the Bechtel Corporation, which has long experience in the desalination water-supply field.

There are several important reasons why the Metropolitan Water District was interested in desalination even though it was already a future beneficiary of the state of California's plan to bring large amounts of water to Los Angeles from the north.

First, the desalting plant is considered a supplemental water resource, which would be extremely important if service from any of the long aqueducts is interrupted. Since each of these aqueducts crosses the San Andreas fault, a well-known earthquake-hazard area, the existence of another source of water already integrated into the system—even if that source is comparatively small—represents intelligent prudence.

Second, the mixing of the 150 million gallons of extremely pure desalted water with water coming in from the Colorado River aqueducts eliminates the need for additional water-softening equipment and will greatly improve the quality of the water reaching the consumer.

Third, the new large-scale plant will provide a true yardstick of desalting sea-water costs for municipal water systems. This is particularly important in southern California. With the state's population growing rapidly, the Metropolitan Water District feels obligated to be certain of the real costs of utilizing desalted sea water before committing itself to possible costs of bringing future water supplies from even further away than now projected.

Fourth, the new plant on Bolsa Chica Island will provide nearby water sources of virtually unlimited potential capacity, since additional modules could be added in the future.

The huge plant, providing 150 MGD of fresh water and 1,800 megawatts of electric power, will be built on a forty-three-acre, man-made island, half a mile off Bolsa Chica State Beach, about thirty-five miles from the center of Los Angeles. In 1965, the cost was estimated at $444 million, of which the federal government would pay $72.2 million, the remainder to be provided by the Metropolitan Water District and three participating utilities. First stages of the project are to be construction of the island and a 50-MGD module. Because the original cost estimates for the nuclear power plant have recently had to be revised, there is now some question as to the amount the utility companies are willing to invest.

President Lyndon Johnson signed the bill authorizing federal participation in the Metropolitan Water District project in mid-1967. He said then that the big plant "will not suddenly make the deserts bloom. But more than anything we have done, it points to the day when lands now dry and empty will sustain life and feed the people of the world."

3

Water and Food

So long as freedom from hunger is only half achieved, so long as two thirds of the nations have food deficits, no citizen, no nation, can afford to be satisfied. . . . For the first time in the history of the world we do know how to produce enough food now to feed every man, woman and child in the world, enough to eliminate all hunger completely. . . . The persistence of hunger during this decade is unacceptable either morally or socially . . . world peace and progress cannot be maintained in a world half fed and half hungry.

The speaker was the late John F. Kennedy, President of the United States, who was opening the World Food Congress in Washington in December, 1963. The Congress met under the auspices of the Food and Agricultural Organization (FAO) of the United Nations.

The delegates were in Washington for two weeks. One of their sessions dealt with the urgent need for more water for agricultural use; special emphasis was placed on the need for irrigation projects, wisely used, to increase the food productivity of arid areas that lacked adequate natural water supplies.

The use of desalination technology was discussed by the commission dealing with water-supply problems, but it was mentioned in terms of hope for some future break-through

63

rather than immediate application to the increased demand for irrigation waters. In 1963, desalination was described by this commission as "still too expensive for agricultural purposes."

The World Food Congress closed on a note of crisis, with Dr. B. R. Sen, Director-General of the FAO, saying that the world had barely thirty-five years in which to "meet the basic needs of 6 billion people who would inherit the earth by the end of the century."

Four years later, Dr. Sen spoke again in Washington, this time to the International Conference on Water for Peace. This time he said, with blunt forcefulness, that the world food crisis "is upon us."

He noted that world population was growing at a rate of $2\frac{1}{2}$ per cent per year, and that it would be necessary to increase the world's food supplies at a rate of $3\frac{1}{4}$ to $3\frac{3}{4}$ per cent per year to meet the growing demand and produce even a slight increase in nutritional standards. The problem was compounded by depletion of North American surplus food stocks to a carry-over level adequate only to counter normal fluctuations of yields in developed countries, and by the fact that food production in developing countries was barely keeping pace with population expansion.

To provide food for the world's masses, the amount of land surface under irrigation must increase from its current level of about 360 million acres to well over 500 million acres by 1985, the FAO maintains. Presently, more than half the acreage on which crops are being grown is in dry, semi-arid, or desert areas where supplementary water supplies could double, triple, or even more extensively increase food production. But existing patterns of land use are likely to continue, Dr. Sen said, "unless some dramatic developments take place such as in the field of desalination of sea water."

Focusing on water problems, for, in his words, "food and water are inseparable," the FAO head emphasized that the increased mineralization of irrigation waters, which has become a severe problem in many countries, and the limits on the ultimate value of conservation measures make it essential that "new fresh water" be found or produced.

Again, he pointed to desalination, calling for intensified research to bring the cost of desalted water to a level where its use will be economically feasible for normal agricultural operations. This level, he and other experts say, is 4 cents per 1,000 gallons—a long way below the current average cost of about 60 cents per 1,000 gallons.

A whole library of books could be written about world food problems and their relation to water supply and irrigation. This chapter in this book will concentrate on just one important question: What can desalting technology do for food production?

The whole answer is not easy to provide. Right now, parts of it are to be found largely in the minds of a few men, some of whom reason on the basis of practical, urgent necessity ("We've just got to have the water no matter what it costs.") and some of whom have developed far-sighted plans for building vast new food factories around nuclear-powered desalting plants to produce food for millions of people on a year-round basis. Other men think other parts of the answer may be found in the test plantings of agriculturalists who seek to breed salt-tolerant crops that can be grown with brackish water (perhaps diluted to individual crop specifications with pure desalted water) or even with pure sea water, which has not been desalted at all. Some researchers seek to apply electrodialysis and reverse-osmosis desalting technology to the problems of salinized irrigation drainage, so that land that is salting up to the point of agricultural uselessness can be reclaimed for food production. Still others, utilizing desalination to supply water for new, developing agricultural methods, such as hydroponics farming and controlled environmental agriculture, are moving forward with exciting, economically imaginable projects, in which high-value vegetables can be grown where they have not been grown before. It is their hope that these methods can some day be applied to basic feed grains, which are the staple part of much of the world's daily diet.

The fact that desalted water today is used primarily for domestic and industrial purposes—and only a small amount is actually being used in agriculture of any kind—is no real indicator of the future. The plans for extremely large desalting plants, said U.S. Atomic Energy Commission Chairman Glenn T. Seaborg at a recent conference in Warsaw, Poland, have "stirred the imagination of many who envision desalted water as the key to bringing into use for agriculture . . . lands . . . having acceptable soil but missing the most necessary ingredient—fresh water."

Food production uses a lot of water. It is estimated that it takes 300 gallons of water to produce 2.5 pounds of bread, 2,300 gallons to produce a pound of beef protein and fat. In his book *The Water Crisis,* published in 1967, editor George A. Nikolaieff projects future patterns of water use in the United States that show agricultural needs consuming 62.6 per cent of all water used in 1980 and 68.6 per cent of all water used in the year 2000. In Japan today, 80 per cent of the water captured from rain or runoff or other sources is used only to grow rice.

The Pioneering Nations

Although Spain has plans for a small use of desalted water for irrigation in one southern area, there are only four nations—Israel, Australia, Pakistan, and Saudi Arabia—where, as this is written, it seems likely that desalination will play any sizable role in the production of food in the near future. (In Australia it will not be a really large one.)

Desalination may be significant in other areas, as desalting plants begin providing water for municipal and industrial use and more of the conventional water supplies are freed for agricultural needs. This is certainly an important use of desalination in total water-supply schemes.

Saudi Arabia provides an interesting case in point. This desert country is one in which desalting will probably play both direct and indirect roles in agriculture.

In reporting to the International Conference on Water for Peace, Prince Mohamed Al Faisal, Director of Saline Water Conversion for the Saudi Arabian Ministry of Agriculture and Water, said his country's short-range goals for desalination included development of water desalination techniques to the point where they can be used for agriculture. "Due to the fact that sea water is virtually unlimited and the fact that there are vast areas in Saudi Arabia along the seacoasts which are suitable for agriculture with no natural resources of water available," he said, "desalination can be an important source of water for irrigation."

Long-range plans, he added, include development and implementation of programs aimed at having desalted water replace, whenever possible, natural sources as the main water supply for municipal and industrial use, so that the natural resources can be used for the growing of food. "With this in mind . . . one can see a possibility for increasing agricultural production," he said.

In the future, too, Saudi Arabia will be looking at the use of brackish water sources made available by improved desalting technology. The nation is also investigating crops that can be grown with desalted water, with an eye toward growing strains that provide the greatest yield per irrigated acre. The Saudi Arabian plans are described in greater depth in another chapter, but it might be mentioned here that plans for investment in desalting facilities already total $40 million for plants that will produce as high as 12 MGD of fresh water.

The philosophy underlying Saudi Arabia's water-development policy is expressed by the Ministry as a desire "to improve the living standards of rural people . . . through investigation and development of soil, native vegetation, surface and subsurface water resources and the development of effective production, marketing, financing and serving facilities to assure livestock growers and farmers a fair price for their increased production."

Another Conference report, by I. Vilentchuk, Vice-Chairman of Israel's Seawater Conversion Commission, told of that country's pressing need for desalted water for agricultural purposes. Israeli farming uses about 80 per cent of the country's currently available water supply, but a large portion of that water is too saline for irrigating salt-sensitive citrus crops, which are Israel's major agricultural export. Because of the need for more food for growing population and export markets, Israel will increase its irrigated areas by 12 per cent by 1970–71, and production of irrigated crops must rise by 34 per cent. The amount of water needed to grow food by 1980 will be 11 per cent higher than the estimated total yield of all available natural water resources after their full development.

Israel is currently operating a 1-MGD desalting plant at Eilat, which has enhanced that Gulf of Aqaba seaport's fishing industry—another source of food; a 250,000-gallon-per-day freezing-process plant in the same city (although this plant may be closed down because the larger plant is producing fresh water at well over the million-gallon design capacity); and an experimental electrodialysis plant, which was designed by the Desalination Laboratory of the Negev Institute for Arid Zone Research and installed in an agricultural settlement in the Negev to reduce the mineral content of brackish well water. In cooperation with the U.N. Development Program, Israel plans to experiment with electrodialysis plants of ten times the capacity of the experimental plant.

According to Vilentchuk, it is estimated that about 40 million gallons of brackish water per day will ultimately be desalted and used for growing selected high-income crops.

The country is also planning construction of a 100-MGD plant on the Mediterranean, which will feed water into the Israel national water grid and greatly expand the available water supply both directly and by diluting waters presently or potentially too salty for agricultural and other purposes.

The United Arab Republic had planned a 5-MGD desalting plant on the Mediterranean, to be used in connection with experimental farming of olives and other high-income crops, but at this writing it is not known if the project can be carried out in view of Egypt's strained economic situation resulting from the 1967 war with Israel.

Australia's plans for utilization of desalination for food-growing purposes are less extensive than those of Saudi Arabia or Israel but are, nonetheless, equally important in their implications for utilization of desalting technology to help solve man's food problems.

Australia is the driest of the earth's land masses, with over 2 million square miles of arid land. The arid zone, however, makes an important agricultural contribution to the country's national economy, for it is the grazing land for about one-quarter of the sheep and one-third of the beef cattle raised "down under."

Much of the ground water in the arid, cattle-growing areas is brackish. Sheep can get along on about one gallon of water per head a day, beef cattle on about five gallons; cattle and horses require a higher degree of water purity than sheep, which have a higher salt tolerance. Australia at this point, according to R. N. Morse of the Commonwealth Scientific and Industrial Research Organization, is interested in the use of solar stills to demineralize the brackish waters in the arid areas to a level where they can create "artificial water holes" and thereby bring more land into use for sheep-raising and, possibly, for cattle-raising.

Stock-watering points can be spaced at two-mile intervals for sheep and six-mile intervals for cattle, their capacity depending on the grazing value of the land in terms of the number of animals it can support with forage. The units will probably be solar stills, such as those being used in Australia for other commercial and industrial purposes, and will produce from 400 to 2,000 gallons of fresh water daily. Estimates are that, by bringing into use for animal production land that is now unusable, solar desalination will bring a return of 18 per cent on the capital outlay involved. This, Morse says, "is a very satisfactory return for the pastoral industry." Further, he points out that solar distillation is the only practical method for isolated grazing areas where unattended operation is required.

Crops from the Coastal Deserts

Another perspective on desalination technology in relation to food production is provided by Peveril Meigs, Chairman of the Arid Zone Commission, International Geographical Union, in his study, "Coastal Deserts, Prime Customers of Desalination," which was presented at the First International Symposium on Water Desalination in 1965. The coastal deserts border the oceans and seas for a total distance of about 20,000 miles. The largest stretch is in the Middle East, along the Red Sea, the Persian Gulf, and adjoining parts of the Indian Ocean and the Arabian Sea, from India to Somalia. Other large stretches are found along the northern and southwestern coasts of Africa on the Atlantic Ocean, the extreme southern part of California in the United States, on the northern Mexican peninsula of Baja California and the northwestern Mexican coastline, and along some of the coasts of South America and Australia.

Among the advantages offered by coastal deserts—as compared to interior deserts—for the use of desalination are the immediately adjacent availability of unlimited supplies of sea water at sea level. The water can be pumped to the desalting plant less expensively than inland brackish or saline waters can be raised from deep wells, and the brine discharged into the ocean much more easily than leftover salt can be disposed of at inland locations. Also, fuel and heavy equipment can be brought in more cheaply by ship than by truck, assuming there are adequate roads for trucks to use. The same availability of coastal shipping capability is advantageous for the export of local products.

Still other advantages include the presence of winds and tides, which may in some instances be resources for power; the availability of fish and shellfish as an ever present source of food; the availability of seaweed of certain types as a possible localized source of human food and livestock feed and as fertilizer and soil conditioner for desert soils deficient in humus. Lastly, coastal desert areas are much more comfortable places to live in than interior deserts.

The climate of coastal deserts varies widely, depending on the distance from the Equator, but many of them are potentially attractive tourist resort areas as well as possible sites for extensive commercial fishing. This chapter will deal with coastal deserts in terms of the contribution they may make to food supply. Their potential for industrial development, with desalination as a source of water, will be explored in the next chapter.

Some of the most productive fishing areas in the world are off the coasts of Peru, South-West Africa and Africa west of the Sahara, and Baja California. But except at a few ports near the mouths of large rivers or streams, practically all the fishing centers—both the large fishing and processing towns and the tiny fishing villages—are hampered by the lack of enough fresh water.

Fresh water is needed for domestic purposes and for processing fish. Canneries or freezing plants use large amounts of water. But the processed fish products are valuable enough to support the cost of desalination, Meigs believes. Some fish-processing centers—Lüderitz in South-West Africa, Salinas in southwestern Ecuador, several small fishing centers in Peru, Puerto Penasco in Sonora, Mexico, on the Gulf of California, and Eilat, in Israel, already get part of their fresh water from desalting plants. Other places where desalination might make possible new or enlarged fish-processing industries are the Gulf of Kutch, in India, the Gulf of Gabès in Tunisia, the Makran coast of Pakistan and Iran, the coast of southeastern Arabia, and the coast of Mauritania. The construction of a solar still to help the fishing industry at Gwadar on the Makran coast is being planned at this writing. India is considering solar distillation in the Kutch area.

For the small fishermen who use their catch largely for subsistence and whose incomes are too small to support desalting plants, Meigs suggests government subsidy of solar distillation plants as part of a developmental program to expand their catch and incomes and provide more food for the surrounding areas.

At the time Meigs made his report, in late 1965, he said that "irrigation agriculture is not a serious customer of desalination under present coast conditions." However, he qualified his statement as follows:

> In a humid climate supplemental irrigation from a standby desalination plant has actually been provided in Guernsey. The only conceivable commercial agriculture using desalinated water in a coastal desert at present is hydroponic farming, where a maximum use is made of the water for intensive production. The outstanding example is on the island of Aruba,

in the Netherlands West Indies, where there is a large production of vegetables for the local population.

Hydroponics farming in Aruba, as Meigs noted, is a highly profitable enterprise, in spite of the fact that the desalinated water used is relatively costly when compared, say, to the price paid for water by a rancher in southern California. Although water represents approximately 20 per cent of the total annual operating cost, the farms make a substantial profit from year-round crops of cucumbers, tomatoes, capsicum, beans, and melons. Cucumber crops are harvested five times a year. After each harvesting, it takes just three days to clean and sterilize the mineral beds in which the crops grow and to put them into production again.

Other applications of desalting technology to coastal desert agriculture are coming into view. One involves a dynamic plan for coastal food factories, discussed toward the end of this chapter. Another envisions feeding dried seaweed or brackish marsh grass to livestock, watered on the product of desalination. Many animals are adaptable to eating salty grasses. In northern Florida, it is not unusual to see cattle grazing calmly while standing hock-deep in marsh waters.

Saline Soils and Brackish Waters

Another far-reaching application of desalination technology may lie in helping to solve the problems of increasing soil salinity in irrigated areas. A recent survey in Pakistan showed 4 million to 5 million acres severely saline, with approximately 100,000 acres a year lost through the spread of waterlogging and salinity. The sugar industry in Guyana along the coastal belt of eastern South America suffers when severe dry seasons lead to the tripling of the salt content in rivers used to irrigate the cane plantations. Although sugar cane tolerates salt easily, the yield drops as salinity rises. During dry spells, Guyanaian cane-growers are forced to waste scarce irrigation water in order to leach the salts out of the ground around the roots of the plants.

The use of desalted water to blend with excessively brackish supplies, or the use of desalination technology to lower the salinity levels of irrigation water sources or to provide periodic supplies of fresh water to leach salt from the irrigated soil, is under study in several countries. In addition, there have been, and are currently, extensive studies in the salt tolerance of various crops and animals and the possibility of breeding especially salt-tolerant species for areas where the only source of water is brackish, or where desalting technology can produce a blend of fresh and sea waters usable for such crops or stock-raising. Already, in Australia, Dr. D. A. Denton and his associates at the University of Melbourne have done extensive research in the salt tolerance of animals. Saudi Arabia plans to import salt-tolerant rice plants from Taiwan to grow, along with local varieties, in an effort to increase the nation's crop yield.

Extensive research in salt tolerance of plants has been conducted for quite some time by the Agricultural Research Service of the United States Department of Agriculture. At the U.S. Date and Citrus Station in Indio, California, the researchers are involved in the long, slow process of trying to breed citrus plants of higher-than-average salt tolerance. They are also working on date cultivation. The date palm is one of the most salt-tolerant fruit trees, and as population pressures increase the demand for fresh water for human consumption, it may be necessary to expand date production with water that is too salty for most other crops in hot desert regions. Summing up the present state of such research in the United States, Dr. C. A. Bower, Director of the U.S. Salinity Laboratory of the Soil and Water Conservation Research Division, Agricultural Research Service, says studies have revealed marked differences in some plant varieties and that the possibilities for breeding increased salt tolerance look good. It is his belief, too, that the use of brackish or partially desalted water for agriculture will be more important than desalted sea water in many areas, because the brackish waters are usually closer to the farmlands involved and hence cost less to get to the fields. However, he says that there will be special situations in which the use of desalted sea water will be practical for growing high-value crops in extremely arid areas where, for various reasons, people have to live. As to the economics of desalination in agriculture, he says, "The permissible cost of desalinated water must be viewed in the context of the cost of obtaining food at a particular location by other alternatives . . . the value approach as opposed to the cost per thousand gallons."

A recent summary by Dr. Hugo Boyko, a noted Israeli agronomist who has been growing plants irrigated with undiluted sea water, showed barley, rye, Italian millet, alfalfa, ladino clover, tramira field mustard, sugar cane, some reeds and rushes, Bermuda grass, dropseed, and salt grass as having good salt tolerance; wheat, oats, sorghum, strawberries, clover, sweet clover, sarson field mustard, sugar beets, sunn hemp, rhodes grass, fodder sorghum, bluestem wheat grass, and seashore paspalum with moderate salt tolerance; and corn, ginger millet, beans and peas, toria field mustard, castor, linseed, sesame niger, cotton, jute, giant star grass, napier grass, and sudan grass with poor salt tolerance.

Dr. Boyko maintains that many plants can thrive on sea water in sandy or gravelly soils with a high degree of permeability. In such soil, the water percolates swiftly through the sand and gravel. The root systems of the plants are well aerated, because there is more space between soil particles than in clayey or silty soil. Salts harmful to plants are quickly washed down into deep layers and have little opportunity to affect the plants. The sodium ion is not absorbed on particles of sand, but it is easily absorbed on particles of clay, where it accumulates and makes the soil so salty that plant growth is harmed.

Dr. Boyko's experiments were conducted on six acres called "The Desert Garden of Eilat." Since 1949, he has grown over 180 plant species, including fruits, hardwood trees, mulberry trees to feed silkworms, and a wild rush that can be used as raw material for making paper. As a result of his experiments, agricultural settlements in the Negev are now using salt water for irrigation purposes with melons and tomatoes.

The Israeli agronomist is one of those who put desalination firmly in agriculture's future. Aside from the possibilities inherent in the use of salty water to grow things in sandy soil, and the possibility—as indicated in Saudi Arabia, for example—that the use of desalted water for cities and industry will free water from other sources for farming, he feels that current efforts to achieve large-scale, low-cost desalting will "contribute significantly to the success of saline agriculture." This prediction is based on the potential availability of excess pumping capacity at big nuclear-powered plants, capacity that could be used to pump sea water directly to saline-agriculture farmlands.

Because of the cost factors, use of desalting technology for agriculture will depend to a large extent on the improvement of irrigation and farming methods. Supplementary irrigation has been found to increase farm yield per acre and to stabilize the basis of farming. British agricultural expert H. Olivier reports that average yields per acre double when farmers switch from dependence on sporadic rainfall to controllable supplementary irrigation.

Olivier points to the great variance in irrigation efficiencies around the world and blames their generally low level on "ignorance at farm levels, out-dated pricing structures of water delivered to the farms," and a general failure to provide water-planning leadership related to the affected soil, water, and seasonal problems or designed to make the best use of existing water resources. He has said also that the "unrealistic and invariably low prices charged for irrigation water, in relation to its economic value, tend to mitigate against incentives for efficient use."

A growing number of experts say that water planners and farmers should look at crop yields on the basis of yield per 1,000 gallons of water rather than per acre. This measurement change implies again the need for coupling water resources with improved farming methods, per se, to make maximum use of available water, whatever that water may cost.

Does Desalting Cost Too Much for Farming?

It might be well to pause here and reflect on the number of times that high cost has been mentioned as a deterrent to the use of desalination for agricultural purposes.

At the First International Symposium on Water Desalination in 1965, J. de Meredieu of the Food and Agricultural Organization of the United Nations, made a forceful statement that has been repeated many times by U.N. experts and others. His arguments ran as follows:

Agriculture uses more water than any industrial process uses. Most industries use less than 100 tons of water for each ton of end product and often return a large amount of the water to the rivers or other source. But agriculture requires several thousand tons of water for each ton of dry matter grown, and the biological processes involved remove a lot of that water from immediate circulation. Obviously, therefore, large additional amounts of water are needed to have an impact on increased agricultural potential, but the cost of this water must be kept as low as possible because of the relatively low value of most agricultural products.

At this point, De Meredieu accepted the possible use of expensive desalted water, with the qualification that its use must be accompanied by "all other elements of intensive farming"—a qualification many of those who quote him in their arguments that desalting costs too much for farming tend to overlook. His words were:

> . . . there is no doubt that desalinated water will remain very expensive for many years to come; irrigation advances based on the process should certainly be organized in such a way as to give the highest return per unit of water applied, rather than the highest return per acre . . . this should be an essential requisite—that desalinated water were applied only where all other elements of intensive farming are already assembled. . . . the most advanced irrigation techniques should be applied.

Noting that the main limitation to large-scale use of desalted water in agriculture is the discrepancy between the cost of the water and the price that farmers can afford—irrigation water is highly subsidized in most parts of the world—he predicted, in 1965, that extensive use of desalted water for irrigation would not develop until there has been a major change in "agricultural productivity or in the price pattern of the main agricultural commodities."

Dr. Joseph Barnea, Deputy Director, Resources and Transport Division, Department of Economic and Social Affairs, who is in charge of the United Nations' exploration of desalination, bases his argument that desalination is still too expensive for agricultural purposes on current costs. "The United Nations is dealing with current problems and current costs," he told this writer. "There are too many variables involved in looking ahead . . . the changing price of energy sources, weather modification, evaporation control. . . . All ground and surface waters should be explored first."

He sees a big field for desalination insofar as water for mining and industry and for blending with agricultural irrigation is concerned. "A country which could not afford 100

or 70 per cent desalinated water for public use could probably afford to provide five per cent for blending," he says.

In his formal report to the International Conference on
Water for Peace, however, he mentioned desalination in only
one agricultural context. It was an important one:

> The supply and use of low-grade and re-processed water, or of
> underground or desalinated water, involves the application
> of a rather high level of technology, and this brings us to one of
> the crucial conditions for an efficient water-management system
> in a water-short country, namely, the adequate availability of
> educated and skilled manpower . . . to handle the numerous
> problems and projects on the water-supply side, as well as ade-
> quately educated water users. Illiterate farmers cannot easily
> gain an understanding of modern water technology. Education
> and training will therefore be one of the difficult preconditions
> for a more efficient water-supply-and-utilization system.

In sharp contrast to the U.N. experts, a dramatic and
hopeful view of the potential of desalination in providing
food for mankind is taken by R. Philip Hammond, Director
of the Nuclear Desalination Program at the Oak Ridge National Laboratory of the U.S. Atomic Energy Commission.

Speaking at a symposium, "Water Production Using Nuclear Energy," at the University of Arizona in early 1966,
Dr. Hammond put the role of nuclear-powered desalination
plants in this context:

> The application of nuclear energy to the task of desalting sea-
> water has changed in a few short years from a dream of a few
> to an important activity. . . . As important as this develop-
> ment is for the future well-being of cities, it becomes insignifi-
> cant in comparison with the impact which a successful appli-
> cation to large-scale agriculture would have on the destiny of
> mankind.

Then he reviewed the basic elements of the problem, many
of which have already been stated in this chapter. The world
presently produces less food than an adequate minimum diet
requires. The doubling of the population within thirty-five

years seems certain. Food output must double, perhaps triple within the next thirty years. There is not enough warm, fertile, well-watered land to be used to double the world food output. Huge increases in fertilizer output, weather modification, water-development projects, farming the sea, cultivation of tropical rain forests, adapting plants to saline water, development of edible algae, massive efforts to increase the yield per acre on presently cultivated land and to bring some areas of fertile arid land into production with desalted sea water—all these hold promise. But, he said, the world is running out of time.

To use desalination effectively for large-scale food production, he told the Arizona conference, the land must have a year-round growing season, in order that investment in water supply and distribution is used at a high load factor; crop utilization of water must be high to minimize the consumption of desalted water. He noted that the Agricultural Research Service has shown that over 5,000 pounds of wheat and corn can be grown per acre-foot of water used, and that yields of these proportions should be readily transferable to irrigation of arid land with distilled water. He compared that figure with present average yields of 1,200 pounds per acre-foot, and he pointed out that such an increase would be equivalent to a 75 per cent cut in the cost of water. Highly efficient sprinkler irrigation, even and controllable, should be used, he urged, along with optimum amounts of fertilizer at the right times in the growth cycle, so that the plants do not produce rank growth, increasing the demand for water without increasing yield. With high purity, less drainage would be required. Because the lack of minerals in desalted water means that evapotranspiration would not increase the salinity of the soil, the water table would not be greatly affected after the initial soil salinity was flushed out.

As to the cost of such an effort, Dr. Hammond said that

there is no real limit to what the industrialized part of the world can afford to commit. "Survival itself would be at stake," he declared.

If, however, one estimated costs on the basis of the under-developed countries providing the arid land, land prepara-tion, and farm labor, with the United States or other aid-giving countries furnishing the water and fertilizer, a $90 billion annual input would sustain 1.5 billion people, the ex-pected population increase by the mid-1980's. This he con-sidered an "encouraging" cost projection, especially since there may be lowered water costs per pound of grain as the nuclear-powered desalination technology improves. Like many others, he believes that time, rather than financial re-sources, must be the limiting factor in the race to make the deserts bloom soon enough to stave off world famine.

At the time of his Arizona speech, it was difficult to define clearly the future role of nuclear desalination for agriculture. No large nuclear plant was in operation. Dr. Hammond said then that there was not enough time to wait to see how the big plants in Russia, Los Angeles, and Israel work, because, "if 20 years or so were available, the nuclear power industry would have matured and a relatively easy spin-off to agricul-tural reactors could be taken. Without it, a parallel program aimed directly at the agricultural energy source may be needed."

Only thirteen months later, however, enough progress had been achieved in the development of existing nuclear tech-nology and specialized breeder reactors for single-purpose desalting plants (as opposed to those required to produce large-scale electric power as well as fresh water) for Dr. Ham-mond to appear before the International Conference on Wa-ter for Peace to present a plan for "extreme agriculture"—food factories built around nuclear desalting plants.

Dr. Hammond asked, when will we know how to make

the deserts bloom with desalination, and how much will it cost? To the first part of the question, his answer was "Now." The Metropolitan Water District plant in southern California, if efficiently turned to food production, would sustain 1 million people, he said. As to cost, which is determined by the cost of the water and the amount of food it raises, he predicted that the plant's expected cost for water of about 5 cents per cubic meter would mean that with 5 cents of water man could raise 5 cents worth of food.

Looking ahead, he dared hope that the cost of fresh water produced by the MWD plant would be halved in ten or fifteen years by continued improvements in both nuclear-reactor and desalting-plant technology, and that genetic improvements in grain seeds would also increase the probable yield twofold in the same period, so that eventually it might cost as little as 1 cent a day to produce the food needed by a single person. "Such costs," he said, "would appear to fall in the range which could make deserts green and give desalination a major role in man's future food supply."

The Promise of Food Factories

The concept of the food factory, presented in that same address by Dr. Hammond at the International Conference on Water for Peace and later by AEC Chairman Seaborg at ceremonies celebrating the Maria Sklodowska-Curie Centenary in Warsaw, is a stunning one.

Because large-scale farming in an arid desert depends on distilled water, which will never be cheap in the sense that rain water or diverted runoff is free, it must differ radically from ordinary farming. The water supply itself makes for big differences, being constant, reliable, and always of high purity. This factor, in combination with other characteristics of an arid desert site, makes it possible to regulate most of the variables that affect normal farming. Thus, a large desert agricultural enterprise using desalinated water can appropriately be called, in Dr. Hammond's phrase, a food factory.

Such a factory would consist of a large, centrally managed farming area equipped for efficient water use, and a nuclear-powered desalination unit. The three main site requirements would be soil, sunshine, and sea. Of course, it would be in an arid area, since otherwise it would already be under cultivation. The land should be fertile (many of the desert areas of the Middle East were once lush farmlands), well-drained, and more or less horizontal. The bigger the number of cloudless days, the better the yield.

The desalting plant would usually be on the seashore, but the rest of the food factory could be anywhere within about thirty miles. Because such a factory must be large enough to compete economically with other food sources, the minimum size might be one that could feed 500,000 people; a larger one might feed 5 million. To feed 1 million people at the assumed grain consumption would require 180 MGD of water after allowing for loss through the ground.

A central laboratory would analyze the soil from each block of land and determine the appropriate fertilizer mix. Pest control would be similarly centralized. Fertilizer would probably be produced on the site. The seed used would be tested and controlled. Irrigation would be monitored by moisture tests. Closed pipes would be utilized to avoid loss of water. (Economic studies indicate that the cost of these measures is far less than that of the water and fertilizer thus saved.)

Food factory crops and their rotation would be determined by soil, local food preferences, and marketing conditions. A favorably located food factory could turn sunshine into food nearly every day in the year. At least two crops could be grown annually on each block of land, with the various blocks seeded in rotation, so that somewhere in the sequence there would be blocks being planted, fertilized, watered, or harvested. Some animal feeding could be done on blocks between crops. Thus, equipment and machinery (or, in developing countries, adequate hand methods) would be used continuously.

This is not mechanized agriculture but agriculture organized to produce the most food for the least water with as little as possible left to chance in the process.

Many hungry parts of the world are primarily rural, with a few large overcrowded cities, scattered small villages, and nothing in between them. Since many countries have some desert areas, these previously uninhabitable regions can attract capital, provide jobs, produce food, and help reduce population pressure in other areas.

Analysis of the hypothetical costs of operating food factories dependent on nuclear-powered desalting plants shows that, according to the type of reactor and evaporator used, the price of water per person fed daily would range from 1.8 cents to 3.6 cents. Capital costs of equipping and maintaining the food factory would add, it is estimated, less than 1 cent a day per person fed. The cost of farm labor, as a real cost, based on the farmer receiving one-third of the crop or its equivalent, would bring the total cost of food-factory crops to a maximum range of about 6 to 10 cents per person fed each day.

Farm-labor costs as such, however, might well be viewed not as cost but as benefit, or product, for the jobs in the food factory represent gainful employment in a new industry on land previously unused. The wages received by the farm labor are a contribution to the local economy.

The keys to success of the proposed food factories are agricultural research devising improved techniques and seeds that produce higher yields, and technological developments in desalting and nuclear reactors that reduce the cost of the water used by the food factory. Each of these keys represents urgent and difficult research and development, which may take ten years or more.

However, many nations can contribute to these efforts. Since the International Conference on Water for Peace, the Israelis have announced a new heat-transfer system, which may, if it proves out, lower the cost of water processed in a large distillation plant. Studies at Oak Ridge presage the impending development of special types of desalination breeder reactors that will produce heat at extremely low costs. Agricultural research is going on all over the world. These three important developments may converge to make possible the building of food factories. If so, the world's deserts may indeed bloom . . . in time.

Controlled-Environment Agriculture

Another exciting prospect, already proving itself in actual practice, is controlled-environment agriculture. Earlier, this book referred to the small, diesel-powered desalting plant at Puerto Penasco, Mexico. This desalting plant has been the focal point around which the University of Arizona, working under a grant from the Rockefeller Foundation, has conducted a highly successful vegetable-growing experiment. The exhaust heat from the plant's motor is used to raise the temperature of the sea water entering the desalination plant. Only about 10 per cent of the intake water is evaporated into fresh water; the remaining warm brine is pumped into the large greenhouse in which the vegetables grow. There the heated water gives off enough water vapor to keep the humidity level at almost 100 per cent. Only in the summer is it necessary to add some of the pure distilled water to the plants in the greenhouse. In addition to the heated brine, the exhaust gases, already used in the desalting plant, are also pumped into the greenhouse, where they increase the carbon dioxide content of the air and hence speed up the rate of photosynthesis and stimulate plant growth. Using one-tenth to one-twentieth of the water required for vegetable farming outside the greenhouse, this pioneer controlled-environment plant grows about 140 tons of vegetables per acre at a cost of less than 4 cents a pound. In addition, the fresh water produced by the desalting plant is piped to a cannery, or bottled and sold to the villagers. The vegetables improve the local diet, and the excess salt water is used for a swimming pool. What's more, some villagers have found well-paying jobs at the experimental plant, which was recently donated to the University of Sonora for continued operation after the experimental phase had been completed.

This project holds tremendous promise for local farming and for large-scale farming if, as the University of Arizona people believe, it can be extended to include the growing of food grains as well as vegetables.

With the development of such schemes as controlled-environment agriculture, hydroponics, and food factories, combined with the availability of the Office of Saline Water's package plans, the steady advance of solar distillation for localized use and cattle watering, and the continuing agricultural research that will find more crops to grow with brackish or partially desalted water, desalination can reasonably be expected to make an important contribution to feeding the hungry.

Farming the desert with desalted water may never replace rain and conventional agriculture, but it may swiftly become a substantial supplement, and, as Dr. Hammond says, "the increasing presence of hunger in the world today makes it imperative that we find such a supplement soon." Saudi Arabia is betting on it for the 1960's, Israel for the 1970's; much of the world may be doing likewise by the late 1970's and early 1980's.

4

Desalting and Industrial Growth

The story of water supply and industry has several sides. Not the least is industry's unfortunate contribution to the pollution and dirtying of existing water sources. Then there is the long history of wasteful industrial use of water, which has placed serious strains on communities in many parts of the world. But here the emphasis will be on how industry's water problems can be mitigated or solved through the utilization of desalination technology.

First, some background.

Most industrial use of water is not consumption, per se. Water used by industry mostly cools or heats, or cleans and washes. Only a very small portion of industrial water intake is actually used as raw material in the manufacture of liquid or other synthetic products, such as bottled drinks, chemical and pharmaceutical solutions, fabrics, paints, and the like. Estimates made by the Business and Defense Services Administration of the U.S. Department of Commerce predict that the water utilized for industrial purposes in the United States, including electric utilities and steam plants, will increase from 125,800 MGD in 1955 to 276,700 MGD in 1980. The amount of water consumed—that is, withdrawn from the supply system as part of the end-product produced by the industry or lost through evaporation—will rise from 7,100 MGD to 24,000 MGD. Projections of future industrial use in other countries are comparable. The water that is not withdrawn from the supply goes back into rivers or lakes or into the ocean as waste water, much of which is ultimately re-used in the same area or by communities farther downstream—if it isn't so polluted that it cannot be re-used.

Nevertheless, American industry's need for water will more than double by 1980. And Japanese water experts predict that their highly industrialized country's demand for industrial water will increase almost four times between 1956 and 1971.

The influence of industrialization on water problems was outlined at the International Conference on Water for Peace by Lt. General A. E. Crahay, Belgium's Royal Commissioner for Water Problems.

In two centuries, he said, Belgium has seen four major industrial revolutions: the use of steam power in the year 1800; the advent of electricity at the end of the nineteenth century; the development of the chemical industry during World War I; and the use of nuclear energy after World War II. During the first two phases, Belgian industry was located near coal mines and raw-material deposits or near transportation that gave access to the raw materials and markets. The volume of water used was relatively unimportant. Now, however, modern industry and giant nuclear power plants find water of prime importance as a raw material, as a cooling medium, as a receptacle for effluent discharge, and as a means of transport by barge or ship.

The figures for Belgian industry are fairly typical: The steel industry uses about 26,000 gallons of water to produce 1 ton of steel, the chemical industry $2\frac{1}{2}$ to $4\frac{1}{2}$ times as much to produce 1 ton of cellulose, the breweries about 3,000 gallons to produce 264 gallons of beer.

Looking ahead, one must add to these increasing water needs of existing modern industry, the needs of perhaps unimagined new industries resulting from general economic expansion. For already industrialized countries, these additional needs may amount to 4 to 5 per cent annually. General Crahay predicts that industrial water needs will double every fifteen years.

How can industry—and a nation's economy—be assured of this increased water supply? Among the sources suggested by Belgium's Royal Commissioner for Water Problems is desalination.

As early as 1964, the U.N. study *Water Desalination in Developing Countries* pointed to desalting as one important answer to the problems posed by General Crahay three years later. It predicted the continued advance of desalting technology, "stimulated [by] the requirements of water for economic development," and said, "Over the past ten years, the progress made . . . has led to substantial reduction in production costs, and the development of new processes gives promise that desalinated water will be within the economic reach of mining, tourist, industrial, household and other groups."

Another broad perspective on desalination in relation to industry was offered by the National Association of Manufacturers and the U.S. Chamber of Commerce in a survey, *Water in Industry*, published in 1965. The viewpoint expressed by these two groups might be characterized as cautious enthusiasm with the checkbook kept firmly out of sight.

In their report, the two organizations pointed to already existing use of desalting technology in industry—evaporators on board naval vessels and ocean liners for half a century; small desalting plants operated by island resort owners and offshore-oil operators. They pointed also to the lowering of the cost of desalted water to one-third of what it had averaged twelve years earlier. Yet, they concluded, the cost of desalting plants was such that it was presently unlikely that municipalities, industries, or agriculture would finance the construction of large sea-water conversion plants in the near future. They did, however, suggest a possible solution in the construction of dual-purpose water and power units, and said that inland sources of brackish water could be made usable for industry by various processes already on the market or in development.

Here, then, are three quite recently expressed viewpoints: Dr. Crahay saying desalting is a solution to industrial water needs of the future; the United Nations predicting widespread application of the technology; two leading American business organizations suggesting it has value but is generally too costly. What is actually happening today seems to fall somewhere between the first two views. The third view already has been disproved by events in Key West, Los Angeles, and other parts of the United States; in Kuwait, Italy, Malta, Mexico, Israel, the Spanish Sahara, Saudi Arabia, Aruba, Bermuda, and the Netherlands.

Industrial desalination has existed for many years. Most of the desalting plants in the United States and Great Britain today provide water primarily or solely for industrial use. Virtually all the plants in the British Isles are producing fresh water for the steam boilers associated with electric power plants—a logical extension of desalting's first important industrial use as a source of water for the boilers of ocean-going steamships. In the United States, too, most of today's desalting plants are associated with electric power plants, although an increasing number provide fresh water for municipal and industrial uses other than power plants. At the beginning of 1967, there were desalting plants with capacities of 25,000 or more gallons per day in thirty-eight of the fifty states, along the seacoasts and the Gulf of Mexico, and on such divers inland waters as the Great Lakes; the Big Sandy River in Kentucky; Cabin Creek, West Virginia; Tanners Creek, Indiana; and a host of other rivers, streams, and lakes.

A 1-MGD plant is being installed for U.S. Steel Corporation in Clairton, Pennsylvania, to demineralize water from the

Monongahela River. This river's mineral content has risen about 700 per cent in the past decade. Another large steel plant using a desalting unit is at Taranto, Italy, where the Italian owners found it more economical to install a 1.2-MGD plant than to dig a canal to bring in the needed water from another source. At Taranto, desalted water is used also by a Shell Oil Company refinery and the Aminova Division of the Nestle Company. These plants have made this former surplus-agricultural-labor area of arid southern Italy a flourishing community. The desalting plants provide water for drinking, for steel and food processing, as well as for the refinery and the steam boilers that power the electrical generators for the mills.

In 1962, when the United Nations made its survey of desalination in developing countries, the great majority of desalination plants studied or operating at that time had gone on stream after 1950, but some older plants were still in operation. A plant built by a railroad in Ecuador had been in operation since 1930, the same year desalting plants were installed at Curaçao and Aruba in the Netherlands Antilles. A plant in Mauritania dated back to 1944, two in Egypt to 1920 and 1935. The two largest plants under construction in 1962 were on Curaçao and in Qatar, and plans had been made for many others, to meet needs such as those of the petroleum industry in Libya and the Netherlands Antilles; an unlikely combination of soft-drink manufacturers and railroaders in Saudi Arabia; tourism in the British Virgin Islands and Southern Tunisia; and domestic and industrial purposes in Israel and Malta.

The U.N. survey found desalting technology used most extensively in the oil and mining industries, other selected industries, the tourist trade, and municipalities. The largest number of plants in existence at the time of the survey were in the oil-exporting countries and territories of Bahrein, Ecuador, Peru, Iran, Libya, Qatar, and Saudi Arabia. Plants associated with mining industries were found in Peru, South

Africa, and the United Arab Republic. In South Africa, for example, a large electrodialysis plant was converting brackish water from flooded mine pits, while in the United Arab Republic, desalting units were providing drinking water for the growing population in phosphate mining areas.

Apparently, many industries were already more willing to pay the price of desalting than the National Association of Manufacturers and the U.S. Chamber of Commerce might have expected. The U.N. report concluded that the relatively high price of desalinated water is usually subsidized by mining or oil companies whose operations produce highly valuable products.

Kuwait is a country whose industrial development has been intimately linked with desalination. Only recently has Kuwait begun to examine potential ground-water resources. At this writing, almost all of the water supply for that oil-rich nation comes from desalting plants, with more than fifty units of various types producing 24.633 MGD of fresh water for the oil plants and their working forces, and 7.5-MGD and 10-MGD plants under construction to provide even more water. Some are government-owned, some company-owned. The Kuwait story, which will be examined at greater length in another chapter, is significant because it underscores the fact that the industrial need for water is not limited to the plant but includes also the community and the men who operate the plant. Without water, there is no labor force. The desalting plant at Ilo, Peru (where there is less rain than in Death Valley, California), supports the community that in turn mans the Southern Peru Copper Company's mines there.

In southern Australia, the largest solar distillation plant at Coober Pedy, supplies water to a small opal-mining settlement, which would otherwise be limited to unpredictable rainfall. The water comes from an underground source 280 feet down and is extremely brackish before distillation. The processed water is sold to the miners and their families and other residents for $7.50 per 1,000 gallons—a high price but one that need makes acceptable.

Where Water Needs Are Growing

There is not time to discuss desalting for industrial purposes on a country-by-country or company-by-company basis, but it is clear that applications of desalination are growing and will continue to grow as nations and industries facing grave water-supply problems seek to expand.

The construction of the large sea-water distillation plant in the extreme southwestern part of the Netherlands, mentioned earlier, is a case in point. The Zeeland-Flanders area is considered attractive for industrial development. It has good labor supply and space, some government aid will be available for the expansion of existing plants or the construction of new ones, and it is favorably located in Western Europe. As the area between Rotterdam and its new harbor complex, Europoort, fills up with industry, economic development must turn to Zeeland-Flanders. Dow Chemical and other large firms are already there.

However, the area faces a rapidly growing need for water—industrial use alone is expected to increase fivefold by 1975. Although rainfall is plentiful, practically all the surface- and ground-water sources are brackish. The major conventional water source for the area has been Belgium. But the Belgians themselves are using more and more water, and the water piped across the Dutch-Belgian border is not sufficiently pure to meet Holland's industrial requirements. Hence, it seemed economically sound and practical to build a desalting plant to convert the salt water of the West Schelde estuary for local uses.

Another area where desalting may soon play a major role is in Istanbul, Turkey, where both domestic and industrial uses of water are rising steadily. Overpumping of ground waters (leading to the intrusion of sea water into ground waters near the coast), as well as population and industrial growth, have caused Turkish water officials to take a hard, realistic look at their water-supply system, parts of which go back to the days of the Ottoman Empire—and even earlier. One dam, built in 1651, is still in use as part of a system that provides about 70 MGD to the city of Istanbul.

Among other projects now being considered in the European section of Istanbul is the desalting of the Cekmece lakes. If this can be accomplished, these two sea-connected lakes will be a major source of new water after 1980. Desalination also may prove helpful in dealing with the increased saltiness of some ground waters.

Water consumption has been rising faster than population; a large part of this increased demand comes from industry. In the city of Istanbul, 21 per cent of the water is used by industry, as compared to 15 per cent in the industrial city of Manchester, 16 per cent in Liverpool, and 7 per cent in Barcelona. It is estimated that industrial use will more than double by 1980, and double again by the year 2000.

The arid Santa Elena Peninsula of southern Ecuador is another example of the relationship between industrial growth and desalination. Bordered by the Pacific Ocean and the Gulf of Guayaquil, the Peninsula in 1962 had a population of 39,100. Oil and salt are the biggest industries on the Peninsula, along with the production of phosphate fertilizer obtained from guano, and the small-scale production of canned sardines, tuna, and shrimp. In addition, tourism brings about 30,000 persons a year into the area for short periods, limited by the water shortages.

The United Nations studied the area in 1962, and indicated that an adequate fresh-water supply could lead to an expansion of both tourism and industry. Fresh-water resources are extremely limited. Two small desalting plants were in operation, one at Salinas, and one at a petroleum camp at Ancón, near La Libertad. The price of water was high, ranging from over $2.00 per 1,000 gallons at Playas and Santa Elena to more than $8.00 per 1,000 gallons for desalted water trucked from the Salinas plant in time of shortage.

One recommendation made at the time by various study groups was the construction of desalting plants to stabilize the water supply and provide water for industrial expansion as well as for the tourist business. Apparently, this is being done, for the 1966 OSW Report shows five desalting plants on the peninsula, compared to the two that existed at the time of the U.N. study.

Needs of Oil, Mining, and Maritime Industries

Peveril Meigs in his 1965 analysis of potential areas for desalination, referred to earlier, indicated the close link between the extractive industries and a financial capability to support desalination projects, adding that petroleum industry processes provide not only an economic basis for the use of desalted water but also cheap fuel in the form of oil or natural gas to provide energy for the desalination plants.

He noted also the link between mining industries and desalination, as did U.N. surveyors, and pointed out that additional desalting plants, or other water resources, would definitely be needed if phosphate and zinc mines near the Red Sea were to be expanded and previously unworked iron ore deposits in the area fully exploited. Many ore deposits elsewhere are undeveloped because of a lack of water for the miners, Meigs stated. Transportation of ore from the big inland mines in Mauritania will require more water than was available in 1965 from natural sources and the old desalting plant at Port Étienne. Other deposits—phosphates along coastal northern Peru and copper in Chile—might be workable if desalted sea water were available to sustain the miners.

Another industry whose future expansion may be closely

linked to desalination is the maritime trade. Desalination can not only support the industries whose products funnel through seaports, but also will supply water for the growing population needed to handle cargoes, service the ships, and provide other services to the maritime workers themselves. The Israeli port city of Eilat is a good example. Desalting there has made possible the expansion of the port, the growth of Israel's fishing industry, and the development of a substantial tourist business.

For the Tourist Trade

Around the world, the development of tourism as an important industry seems inextricably tied to an adequate supply of potable fresh water. Most large groups of tourists come from the more highly developed nations, where they are accustomed to high living standards. Those standards include good water. Tourists who stay any length of time drink local water, beer, and soft drinks, bathe or shower, wash their clothes, and may need a good hospital. If the local water is poor, tourists do not stay; they pass through, pausing only briefly for sightseeing and some limited souvenir shopping.

Tijuana, Mexico, has been mentioned as an area that has long attracted one-day visitors from north of the border, but now, with a big new desalination plant to provide enough good water to support all local facilities, it hopes to welcome longer-term vacationers. In the Caribbean, desalted water is an increasingly important part of the water supply. There are two desalination plants in the Bahamas and five in the Virgin Islands. Tourists have lately been making more and more use of the five desalting plants on the Canary Islands off the coast of Africa.

In some water-short areas, the promotion of tourism has led to the establishment of double-piping systems. Brackish or sea waters are used for purposes other than drinking and cooking, while desalted water (or other fresh water) comes from the kitchen and bathroom faucets.

Like the oil and mining industries, tourism seems to be quite able to absorb desalination costs in the daily or weekly hotel charges to the tourists. One large Bermuda hotel recently built a new desalting unit to augment an older one with a daily capacity of 167 cubic meters, whose output had been supplemented by water delivered by ship from New York at a cost of more than $12.00 per 1,000 gallons.

At the beginning of 1967, there were seventeen desalting units on Bermuda, including those at Kindley Air Force Base and McKinley Field. One supplies the King Edward VII Hospital, five are associated directly with big hotels. The Bermuda water shortage is so chronic that every house is required by law to have water catchment areas on the roof. The desalting plants are beginning to relieve the island of dependence on irregular rains and shipment of water from New York at high cost.

The island of Malta, in the Mediterranean, has rushed the construction of a 1.2-MGD desalting plant, built by Aqua-Chem, Inc., of Milwaukee, to provide fresh water for tourists who, it hopes, will fill the gap in the island's economy created by the forthcoming closing of the big British naval base there. Negotiations are under way for a second plant of similar size.

Catalina Island off California has for some years used a seawater desalting plant to provide water for the weekend tourist influx. The small Cape Verde Islands off the coast of Africa in the Atlantic Ocean are becoming Portugal's major example of the use of desalination to encourage tourism. Already, a desalting plant provides water for the airport on the all-but-rainless islands. In addition, a plant producing about 600,000 gallons of water daily is to be built at Mindelo by 1969.

Discussing this project during the International Conference on Water for Peace, M. Neto Valente of the Portuguese Overseas Ministry noted that the Cape Verde Islands were "discovered" five centuries ago, but, he said, "have not yet been discovered by tourists, who can find there a place of tranquility—of nature and of souls—untouched by war. Sea water made drinkable is revolutionary, but it belongs to a technical revolution, which does not affect tranquility. It is water for peace."

Solar distillation is being used to augment the water supply on the coral islands and atolls of the South Pacific, where the maximum elevation is rarely more than fifteen feet above sea level. The islanders obtain their cash incomes from the production of copra and from fishing the lagoons or the sea. Water supplies were previously obtained by each family from wells or rainfall collected on the rooftops of the small houses. The well water was frequently contaminated by salt water from the ocean, or by surface drainage containing various wastes and minerals.

The Health Department of the South Pacific Commission set up a cooperative arrangement with the University of California to study desalination for the low islands. The study recommended the installation of small solar distillation plants similar to those already in use at Rangiroa in French Polynesia, at Nandi in Fiji, at Tarawa, and on an island near Port Moresby, New Guinea.

While these islands may not, at first, seem directly applicable to tourism, the lands of the trade winds have long had a beckoning appeal for travelers. One major American airline has optioned land in the South Pacific for the construction of tourist hotels. With a good supply of potable water, the low islands could become important way stations on the tourist map of the world.

Other Applications

There are many other variations on the application of desalting technology to industry. The Aerojet-General Von

Karman Center in Azusa, California has been developing small reverse-osmosis units. One is now being used to provide fresh water for a Navy photographic laboratory in Washington, D.C. Another Aerojet-General unit is being used to purify water for re-use by chemical and petrochemical plants in Odessa, Texas. Pepsi Cola International has purchased a 12,000-gallons-per-day electrodialysis unit to provide high-quality water from saline sources for its bottling plant at Al Khobar, Saudi Arabia. Similar plants have been used by soft-drink bottlers in the Near East and Europe since 1957, and one is being used to desalt "stickwater"—a liquid by-product of fish-meal manufacturing—to produce protein at a plant in Peru. Desalination enables the producer to take additional fish-oil protein from the residue before discarding it.

One major water problem related to industry is the pollution of water supplies by industrial effluents. Desalting technology is already moving in this field. Coal mining, for example, produces mine acids that have made many streams and rivers unusable without expensive treatment by downstream communities. Westinghouse is adapting desalting processes to the mine-acid problem in cooperation with the state of Pennsylvania. This firm is designing a pilot plant that will treat 5 million gallons of mine-acid drainage daily. The decontaminated water will be sold for about 33 cents per 1,000 gallons, well under the cost of water supplied by many Pennsylvania municipalities. The plant will use locally available coal as its heat source, thereby stimulating the local economy while producing enough fresh water for a city of 50,000 people.

Another industry that has been frequently criticized for polluting waters with its refuse is sulphite paper manufacturing. At the Consolidated Paper Company in Appleton, Wisconsin, a vapor-compression desalting unit turns out 30,000 pounds of fresh water hourly with a process that concentrates the used sulphite liquor while reclaiming contaminants that are sold at a profit. Oddly, these salable by-products include an ingredient used for making vanilla extract and a mud-dispersal agent for oil-well drilling.

In still another important case of contaminated waste water, the Brookhaven Atomic Energy Commission Laboratory on Long Island uses desalination technology to evaporate radio-active waste waters, making it simpler to dispose of the con-centrated residue by burying it at sea in small, sealed, lead containers.

This application of desalination technology also works in reverse, of course, making it possible for industries with specialized water needs to utilize brackish or sea waters or local water supplies, which may not be suitable for industrial processes. The manufacture of transistors, certain pharma-ceuticals, and some chemicals requires absolute purity. (Thus, at Abbott Laboratories in North Chicago, a 140,000-gallons-per-day vapor-compression distilling unit provides pure water for the preparation of intravenous solutions.) How critical this problem may be for a firm is illustrated by the experi-ence of a Brooklyn company—a manufacturer of surgical sutures packaged in sterile water. A few years ago, it moved to Connecticut to expand its plant, only to find the water there too mineralized to be usable. The plant had to move back to Brooklyn. Today, it could have installed an appro-priately sized desalting unit and stayed in Connecticut.

The recycling of water for re-use is done in two ways. In one, used water goes back into the river, lake, or underground source. If it has been purified by the industry or municipality that first used it, it can be re-used downstream, or over again by the same community or industry. The other way, called closed recycling, sharply reduces the amount of water taken from supply sources for use in an industrial plant. For ex-ample, the Kaiser Steel Plant at Fontana, California, recycles its water supplies internally. Its water intake per ton of steel is 1,100 gallons, against a national steel-industry average of 65,000 gallons.

The possibility of large-scale re-use and recycling makes it almost impossible to forecast accurately industrial water needs for the future. But the installations required will probably be too costly for many firms to make individual installations. Industrial water use will probably continue to be wasteful, and the need for more and more water can be expected to continue. Obviously, desalting technology, scaled as it is from small portable units to multimillion-gallon capacity, will play an ever larger role in helping to meet growing needs.

In 1965, Andrew J. Biemiller, Director of the AFL-CIO Department of Legislation, wrote to Senator Henry M. Jackson, Chairman of the Senate Committee on Interior and Insular Affairs, which was holding hearings on Office of Saline Water appropriations. Biemiller first quoted President Johnson's message to the Senate, in which the President said, "By pressing ahead with a vigorous program of economic desalting to meet our ever-growing domestic needs for water, we will at the same time provide the technology which can be shared with other nations. This technology could provide the key that will unlock the door to economic growth for many of these nations."

Then Biemiller added:

> Organized labor shares the President's hopes for the early fruition of this Nation's 12 year old water distillation program. In 1961, in supporting the legislation which was enacted into law as the present desalting program, we urged that converted saline water be made competitive with other sources in cost before 1980. If such a goal is not achieved, we stated, local and regional water shortages which already spot various sections of the Nation will seriously affect the national welfare.

Already, industries are shying away from water-short areas of the Southwest. The AFL-CIO was putting it on the line.

Water shortages mean loss of jobs. Desalting produces water. Desalting means jobs.

French scientists J. L. Burgaud and C. Oger, of the Société Saint-Gobain Techniques Nouvelles, put it another way in a recent paper, "Industrial Waters: A Method for the Study of Problems of Each Industrial Site." They wrote: "Water has become a basic criterion for the construction of a new plant; water problems come up in the site selection, in the conception of circuits and even at the process level."

For many parts of the world, either lacking water or rapidly running out of water, the competition to provide sites for new industrial plants or tourist facilities may be lost already, unless, like the Dutch at Zeeland-Flanders, they go ahead with the construction of desalting plants, so that they can guarantee a usable water supply to the engineers charged with site selection.

5

Desalting and the Developing Countries—A Perspective

In the already highly developed and industrialized nations of the world, desalting for domestic, industrial, and agricultural needs can help make possible continued growth and development by supplementing water supplies that are becoming inadequate in both quantity and quality. In the developing countries, the role of desalting may well be revolutionary. Desalted water—in the right places—can elevate standards of living, eradicate waterborne disease, bring new industries, and turn wastelands into food factories.

Before discussing the specifics of how and where this revolution can be achieved in the developing countries, it is necessary to place desalting technology within the perspective of water planning, per se. Without comprehensive water planning in a framework of total national planning, the capital investment in desalting plants could well be wasted by producing only spotty, localized advantages. This chapter, therefore, will deal more with water planning than desalination and its application—and, to a large extent in the pages following, the water-planning experts will be allowed to speak for themselves.

When the leaders of a developing country plan its future, water supply must have very high priority on the agenda. Such planners have one dubious advantage over their colleagues in more socially and economically sophisticated nations. They are not dealing with a need to correct the past. They are not dealing with problems of large populations who are running out of water because the available supply is being exhausted, or polluted. Nor do they face the need for costly rehabilitation of large and no longer adequate water-supply systems.

True, they face shortages, but ones stemming from a different set of causes. Water shortages in developing countries may be the result of a general lack of supply systems or the existence of systems designed to meet only the relatively small-scale needs of former colonial powers or foreign investors for the exploitation of natural resources in a given location. They also face shortages created by climate, natural aridity, or the simple fact that no one ever bothered to seek or exploit water resources within their borders. In some cases exploitation was not possible, since, until recently, no technology existed that could make an abundance of sea water or brackish water usable when no other water was available near populated areas.

Because they have little to undo, so to speak, the developing nations have a golden opportunity to develop their water resources through the utilization of new knowledge of modern techniques, which are becoming increasingly available to them through such world-wide scientific efforts as the International Hydrological Decade. Each of these countries has a variety of choices from which to shape the specific plan that can do the most for its people. Nations whose peasants or nomadic tribes now scratch a subsistence living from the soil can become important sources of food for the world's exploding population. Their new industries can be built in desirable locations, their cities established or expanded with improved standards of living.

But to attain such goals, planners in developing countries must apply a total concept that includes both the source of the water and the way in which it will be used. Expensive modern water-supply technology, if it merely serves industries that do not recycle water or do not adequately treat wastes, cities that spew filthy wastes into streams, or farmers who perpetuate antiquated agricultural methods, is not accomplishing all it might. And a limited, project-by-project approach is a path to minimal achievement when substituted for truly national or regional water planning.

Turkey is a developing country, though one with a long history as a nation. Two of its water planners, Kemal Noyan and Turhan Şenoğullari of the Ministry of Energy and Natural Resources, provide an excellent introduction to a perspective on water planning when they say that the shortage of investment capital in most developing countries makes the determination of priorities almost as important as the meeting of the many requirements facing the nation.

Lack of investment capital can lead planners to use water resources first for irrigation and power generation, because of higher cost-benefit ratios and quicker repayment on investment. Countries in which this happens also tend to expedite the economic development of populated areas before furnishing them with a sufficient supply of water. As a result, existing water systems in the cities cannot provide the water needed by a growing population. The consequences are grave. As Noyan and Şenoğullari picture it, living standards decline, and waterborne disease increases. Economic growth becomes limited. Previous neglect makes necessary more costly and complex construction projects, wasting money and extending the water shortage for unnecessarily long periods of time. Individuals left on their own to augment inadequate public water supplies use too much ground water. In turn—in areas near the coast—sea water intrudes into ground water, and costly preventive or corrective measures become necessary.

In the Philippines, according to Santos B. Rasalan of the Philippines Fisheries Commission, just such a problem can be traced to faulty utilization and management of water resources. Salt-water encroachment on existing water supplies in and around Manila and other big cities is caused by uncontrolled use of ground water on the part of industry and residents, and by indiscriminate discharge of wastes into streams and rivers, drainage of swamps or marshes, dredging and deepening of waterways, and faulty well-digging—all of which combine to disturb the salt- and fresh-water equilibrium. The problem of water encroachment, he says, "looms as a major threat that may jeopardize the Philippines' efforts for economic development."

The foregoing indicates some part of what water-supply planners have to cope with in developing countries. How simple it would be if they need only telephone their nearest desalting plant manufacturer, order model number so-and-so, clear the land for construction, announce to the public that on such-and-such a date the country or town or region will be hooked up to a desalting plant and that then social and economic progress will ensue! But progress doesn't happen that way.

A U.N. Viewpoint

Many obstacles lie in the path of the water planner. There is, first of all, the necessity to examine the broad social and economic context within which he seeks to provide solutions for his nation. One of the most cogent summaries of the planner's parcel of problems, dilemmas, and frustrations is offered by Dr. Joseph Barnea, one of the foremost U.N. experts on water supply. Although this writer and others do not always agree with some of his specific attitudes concerning desalination—as indicated elsewhere in this and other chapters—there is no gainsaying that Dr. Barnea, perhaps more than any other person in the water field, has had a great deal of practical experience in assaying the water problems of the developing nations of the world.

Discussing water policy from the U. N. point of view, Dr. Barnea says that

> . . . in water-short areas, the evaluation of priorities in water needs, both in the near and the long term, is a basic problem of water policy. One prerequisite for appropriate evaluation of needs is the development of an awareness of the problem on the part of the responsible Government officials, planners of industry and many others, so that this awareness might pervade all spheres of economic activity. For example, water-intensive industries should be eschewed, where possible, in favor of industries that require less water, and the use of water in mineral resources development and processing should be reduced through application of the new methods of dry ore separation and concentration.
>
> If exploration for new water resources is undertaken, the new resources should not automatically be earmarked for agricultural purposes. This is a mistake which is frequently being made in water-short developing countries not only by national authorities but also by the providers of external technical assistance. In many instances, new water supplies opened up at heavy cost are allocated to agriculture even when they represent the only remaining unused sources of water. The future re-allocation of these resources will present a difficult social problem which could have been avoided.

In the face of the demand for food for an exploding world population, there are those who see agricultural needs for water as paramount (and as the chief argument for application of desalination technology). However, Dr. Barnea's viewpoint has validity. Comprehensive water and water-use planning are necessary from the point of origin—an underground aquifer, a river, a desalting plant—to the city dweller's kitchen tap or public well and the small farmer's irrigation and cultivation methods. Agriculture is only one consideration.

Dr. Barnea continues, adding that

. . . allocation of as yet unutilized water does not arise in water-short areas, particularly in densely populated areas, as frequently as the problem of an existing water regime of such a nature as to constitute an obstacle to economic development. Many developing countries among those that are water short are faced with the situation wherein primitive agriculture absorbs most of the available water, leaving an insufficient amount for the potential competing demand of alternative classes of consumers. This is one of the most difficult problems governments have or will have to face, particularly in view of the present rapid urbanization and introduction of industry, including water-intensive industries. . . .

Obviously, the reallocation of water in water-short countries is as much a social question as one of economics. A reduction in the extent of agriculture may create unemployment among agricultural workers, which is tolerable in most countries only if this manpower can be absorbed by industry or other sectors of the economy. However, the reduction of agricultural production may lead to the necessity of importing food and other agricultural products, with possibly unduly adverse foreign exchange effects upon the economy as a whole—except in the case of petroleum-exporting countries, which do not have a shortage of foreign exchange.

Plainly, the problem of water supply in developing countries—or any country, for that matter—is not something to be dealt with by the hydrological engineer alone. It is a matter of total national policy—social, economic, and political. Frank DiLuzio, formerly Assistant Secretary of the United States Department of the Interior, has listed three principal needs common to developing countries: roads, schools, and water. Roads make possible the transport of farm and industrial products to and from the market place. Schools feed the human spirit and raise the level of the population's social aspirations and capabilities. Water means survival and growth.

Thus, in the developing countries, the cost of the water supply becomes the basic determinant in all planning.

Pointing out the need for reliable forecasts of changes to be expected in water demands in developing countries, Dr. Barnea says that

> . . . forecasts must indicate not only the quantities of water that will be required but also water quality and the range of water prices which the end-users of this water will be able to afford. Once a reliable long-term forecast of this kind has been prepared, the Government of a water-short country is likely to recognize that its economic planning must largely be determined by water costs and water availability.

Water costs are the subject of Chapter 7. Three other major factors must be taken into account in planning a developing country's water resources.

One is the possible use of low-quality brackish or saline water for certain types of agriculture and as a cooling agent in power plants and other industries. "Brackish and saline water will have wider applications with further progress in research, which fact should be taken into account in water resources and economic planning," Barnea says.

A second factor is the need for skilled manpower. On this subject, Barnea points out:

> The supply and use of low-grade or reprocessed water, or of underground or desalinated water, involves the application of a rather high level of technology, and this brings us to one of the crucial conditions for an efficient water-management system in a water-short country, namely, the adequate availability of educated and skilled manpower, such as geologists, engineers and economists, to handle the numerous problems and projects.

This need for trained people was emphasized at the International Conference on Water for Peace in Washington. Many countries have started programs for building the necessary cadres with high-level skills. In tiny Yemen, 250 employees have been trained for the local water-supply system with the cooperation of the U.S. Agency for International Development. Hundreds of engineers from developing countries attend nine- to twelve-month water-supply training programs at the University of North Carolina's school of sanitary engineering. At the same time, developing countries are undertaking related education at the user level. Venezuela, for example, has created local water boards to oversee the distribution and use of water supplies. Mexico has extensive user re-education programs.

Barnea again underscores the need for trained technicians when he talks of the third factor, maintenance:

> It takes time—and funds—to raise a country's level of education and to train skilled personnel. But some of the water problems are so urgent that they call for a much earlier solution. Therein lie many problems and past mistakes. It is useless to have groundwater-supply systems constructed or desalination plants built unless skilled manpower is available to operate and maintain them. In many cases, installed facilities have deteriorated and groundwater diesel units have broken down and been left unattended. Where water needs are urgent and the local skilled manpower is not available, Governments will have to undertake the establishment and operation of repair and maintenance services, which could later on be taken over by local personnel. The cost of establishing and running repair and maintenance facilities must of course be included in the calculation of the costs of the water projects.

A Guatemalan Critique

One of the criticisms frequently directed at manufacturers who build desalination plants or other water projects under "turnkey contracts"—in which the manufacturer assumes complete responsibility for the construction of the plant—and at foreign technical missions is that they do not sufficiently involve and train local engineers and operating personnel. Inasmuch as most major water projects in developing nations involve foreign aid or technical assistance, this is a critical problem. Perhaps the most pointed statement of it has been made by Samuel B. Bonis of Guatemala's National Geographic Institute.

Noting that his country's water needs are such that national water programs in Guatemala must be keyed to some sort of international cooperation and assistance, he says:

> . . . the most critical problem in underdeveloped nations is the lack of competent and dedicated technicians to initiate and carry through programs, no matter how modest. Low salaries, limited opportunities and lack of intellectual stimulation are usually cited as causing an exodus of talent from these countries to regions of higher industrial development. The technicians who remain in their country attribute their inactivity and lack of effectiveness to insufficient funds and governmental indifference. These factors lead to the disillusionment and stagnation of national technicians; nevertheless, the enterprising and dedicated technician can always make some important contribution, starting from simple, but necessary data collection, assembling and evaluating previous investigations, bibliographies and cooperation with other agencies. This type of work requires a minimum of expenditure and dependence upon others. It is a sad fact . . . that not even this type of work is being done. A great amount of money and time is invariably lost to the nation because this basic information is not readily available when a project is begun, and is reflected in an inflated cost of feasibility studies and of the projects themselves.

Foreign-assistance programs in water-resource projects can make an important additional contribution to the long-range progress of a developing nation by creating a reservoir of enthusiastic and skilled indigenous technicians to carry forward and develop new projects. Such education and training is usually written into the project contract. But, Bonis comments,

> . . . in practice this phase is often abandoned in the face of difficulties which are delaying the entire project. Too often

expediency demands that the educational aspects of a program be sidestepped in order to attain the material objectives. It is frequently much easier to leave showcases of fancy equipment and glossy reports than to deal successfully with the problem of training local personnel and infusing them with the spirit necessary to overcome the obstacles found in a non-technical society.

This is not all the fault of the contractor or foreign-aid group, Bonis is quick to admit. The few scientists and engineers in a developing country are usually found in major urban centers and have little tradition of arduous field work. Host governments are prone to exaggerate the caliber and number of technical experts available, in order to provide an attractive counterpart group.

We have all witnessed the dismay of project managers upon leaving the fantasy of the written contract and the preliminary honeymoon visits. The counterpart technicians prove to be non-existent, unavailable, untrained, or worst of all, unwilling. The high-ranking liaison man appointed by the host government who is the indicated person to iron out these difficulties, too often proves to be a bureaucrat not sufficiently interested or capable to perform his essential role. . . . Too often visiting experts do all the technical work, local professionals acting as the service organization or as harmless onlookers fulfilling the contractual obligations of counterpart technicians.

Bonis offers several recommendations, beginning with the basic step of adopting the philosophy that training, experience, and responsibility for local personnel are as important as the material objectives of a project:

Foreign assistance should be geared to the effective participation of local technicians. As local personnel increase in number and caliber, so may the projects become more sophisticated. . . . It is important that these projects are not merely training exercises, but much-needed works which require professional standards, decisions and responsibility.

. . . training of local professionals is for naught if they subsequently leave the country or enter more lucrative fields foreign to their profession. This is especially common among the more capable technicians. Higher salaries would help keep many of these people, but of equal importance is a love for their profession and a desire to advance their field within their own nation. The visiting expert should do all possible to create this dedication.

The Value of Local Advice

It may be fortunate for the evolution of desalination technology as a part of the water-supply program of developing nations that it does not take a great many technicians to operate a desalting plant and adjoining power plant. As few as half a dozen people can run a 1-MGD plant. Not many more are needed for one that produces 100 times as much water. However, national water planners must remember that the desalination plant is just the water input to the system. Many more skilled people are needed to man and maintain the supply system, and at the water-use training level.

Local engineers can be extremely important in advising on the design of a desalting plant. For example, a plant was recently installed in a country where coal, locally available at relatively low cost, was to be used to provide the energy for heating the sea water in the evaporators. As part of the installation, the manufacturer included an automatic, endless-chain, coal-feeding apparatus. Although it added to the cost of the plant, it was never used because of the local tradition of carrying coal by hand. A local consulting engineer, familiar with local customs, could have pointed out that, for both social and economic reasons, it would be preferable to utilize local labor to bring the coal to the furnaces.

Local technicians can also coordinate the work of adapting

the local water system to the new input of desalted water, planning for needed storage facilities, and helping to prepare the beneficiaries of the new source of fresh water by devising distribution systems and participating in the development of related industrial and agricultural water systems, which may utilize part of the water directly or by blending with other water resources. Local engineers can also be educated in plant maintenance so that the plant does not stand idle until parts can be fabricated and installed by an engineering team from the factory.

Water in the Wet Tropics

Some of the other problems inherent in water planning in developing countries can be found in the words of Edward Davies of Freetown, Sierra Leone. His subject is water resources development in the wet tropics, which encompass approximately 30 per cent of the world's population and include large areas of South America, the southernmost parts of North America, Central Africa, South Asia, and a majority of the Pacific Asiatic Islands and northern Australia. The wet tropics are characterized by minimum subsistence levels, which are easily achieved but hard to surpass. The emergence of a relatively large number of newly autonomous countries within the wet tropics tends to diversify the solution of their common problems. Davies says:

> Characteristically these countries are mostly at the stage of progress where their water resources may be developed to produce the often politically advantageous immediate local benefits as well as to establish firm bases upon which long term benefits may be founded. By contrast with the more developed countries, economic activity is more marked in the resource industries; mining and other extractive industries provide a large fraction of the national revenue, food production being usually at a level less than is necessary to ensure that each resident can have a well-balanced diet. In their desire for progress

and development, national interests emerge in two conflicting schools of thought; the one school postulates that agricultural expansion must be a by-product of a conscientiously stimulated growth on the basis that the terms of international trade tend to perpetuate the economic dependence of primary producers and that increased agricultural production and rising living standards may increase the birth rate and consequently the population pressure; less clearly, industrialization and urbanization come to be regarded as synonyms for wealth and comfort; the other school postulates simply that with the ever present threat of famine, staved off temporarily by hand-outs from the more developed countries, economic policy must be directed primarily towards stimulating agriculture. This conflict is important in the context of water resources for two main reasons: firstly, because it may become so intense that it does in fact inhibit progress in any direction; secondly, because when kept within bounds, it helps to determine the scale of priorities allotted for different classes of water use.

Progress demands that the long term development of water resources be alloted an order of priority in a field of inter-related and competitive needs, all mutually dependent, all screaming for recognition and financial support from strictly limited and virtually inelastic national revenues.

Davies lists some additional factors with which the water planner for the wet tropics must cope: "the absence of a political and intellectual climate harmonious for the application of the needed skills; the lack of organization and data indispensable for early and effective development; the absence of capital of the quantities needed under advantageous conditions; the non-allocation of a high priority both at the topmost planning levels and at all levels throughout the nation."

Some Present Necessities

A recent study by the World Health Organization (WHO) showed that only 10 per cent of the urban dwellers in seventy-five developing countries are supplied with water piped to their homes, and this is more often than not intermittent service lasting only a few hours daily and with inadequate quality supervision. It is estimated that inadequate drinking-water supplies are responsible for perhaps 5 million infant deaths each year.

In countries where such water-supply conditions exist, it is doubtful that even rudimentary waterworks construction is keeping up with population growth. In the WHO study, Dr. H. G. Baity suggested that "it becomes logical to give [some] water to as many people as possible rather than to give a perfect supply to a few."

Two University of North Carolina engineers, Daniel A. Okun, who heads the Department of Environmental Sciences and Engineering, and Frederick E. McJunkin, Director, International Program in Sanitary Engineering Design, have challenged this statement, saying, "If one accepts Dr. Baity's argument, the . . . engineer, applying . . . 'standard practice' within development countries, would be a wastrel where needs are so great that any waste is inequitable . . . perhaps even immoral." But they added, "The result sought is an adequate amount of safe water for people—the more people, the better result. The designer and developer of community water supplies in developing countries, even more than his counterpart in developed countries, must . . . challenge sacrosanct standards . . . must be imaginative and exercise the ingenuity demanded by limited resources."

In this respect, Sierra Leone's Davies suggests that

. . . whilst the larger and more complicated projects require a large mass of hydrological data for realization, there is a fertile field for the development of water resources in providing usable water for small or medium-sized rural communities. The provision of such water supplies can be made one of the first steps in bringing isolated and less productive areas of a developing country into the field of the national economic effort. The capital lay-out involved is usually, in relation to the material and psychological benefits to be derived, very small; individuals in the village community often contribute of their time and labor in developing such "self-help" schemes. Health competition grows between neighboring communities, the horizon of wants is extended and often begets greater output at the grass-roots level of the community.

For the developing country, desalination technology meets the flexibility criterion suggested by Okun and McJunkin, and it can be utilized in the kind of small-scale projects suggested by Davies. Desalting equipment comes in a variety of shapes and forms. It can be permanently installed, or it can be mobile, moving from village to village on trucks or railroad cars, or along the coast on shipboard. A community need have only two elements: a source of sea or brackish water and storage capacity. Any kind of distribution system can be hooked up to the storage facilities. Small solar distillation plants can be erected with local labor and materials. Even piping for a distribution system can be manufactured locally if one uses newly developed pipelines made of sand and plastic and asbestos.

Larger plants can be permanently installed and sized to meet the current and projected need. The initial investment in an electrodialysis or reverse-osmosis or ion-exchange plant may seem high, even if it is not large, but it may turn out to be considerably less than the cost of a dam and reservoir, with attendant pipelines and filtration facilities, and it can be expanded with additional units of relatively low cost, whereas the building of more dams is costly and may necessitate moving water from greater and greater distances. The fact that desalting plants can be linked to existing power plants or built with new power plants that will also supply electricity to a region, has other plus factors for a developing country.

Where there are extensive but saline ground-water resources available, depending upon the degree of salinity involved, limited desalination can produce enough pure water for blending purposes to make large amounts of hitherto un-usable ground water acceptable for irrigation, industry, and home consumption.

Who Makes the Decisions?

The over-all context within which decisions concerning desalination should be made in a developing country leads to an important basic question. Who makes the decisions? Dr. Barnea of the United Nations offers the following an-swer:

> The Government in a water-short country will ultimately have to accept responsibility for overall water management. This may require the adoption of new water legislation and the abolition of existing water rights, including, where necessary, the water rights of individuals, villages and municipalities. Furthermore, and this is most important in the long run, it will require the centralization of decision making at a high level inside the Government. In most cases, a number of de-partments, such as the Ministries of Agriculture, Public Works, and Public Health, deal with different aspects of water re-sources. While these Ministries may retain many of their func-tions, it is essential that a Central Water Authority be es-tablished, preferably attached to the Prime Minister's office, charged with the following functions: short and long-term planning of water development and use; establishment of prior-ities; evaluation of major projects; allocation of water and es-tablishment of uniform water costing and pricing methods and their application. The Central Water Authority will thus be in a position to establish guidelines and a long-term water policy in conformity with the needs of the country and its de-velopment goals. It will and should have the necessary au-thority to impose its policies on the various Ministries and other bodies dealing with water but it should not be burdened with the carrying out of engineering or geological studies, ex-ecution of projects, responsibility for maintenance and repair of facilities, collection of revenue, training of personnel, and the many other necessary functions within the wide field of water resources and water use. The Authority should not be

attached to a Ministry since a Ministry—even the Ministry for Agriculture in a country whose agricultural sector absorbs the bulk of the water supplies—has relatively limited objectives and concerns.

Dr. Barnea's concept of a Central Water Authority is sound, but not often found. In Saudi Arabia, Israel, and Mexico, water planning is high in the national hierarchy. In the United States, it is fragmented through many agencies of the federal government and thousands of state and local units. In many other countries, it is linked with public utilities and agriculture. The newer among the developing countries have an opportunity to separate water-planning functions from other concerns at the start and give them the status they require. Then, in Dr. Barnea's words:

> Once the Authority begins functioning its decisions will have very far-reaching implications for the economy of the country as a whole and for the overall planning of economic development. The Authority will find that rapid technological changes, new resource discoveries, and shifts in population as a result of declining as well as growing industries will dictate flexibility in water planning, and concern with policies and changes in needs, technologies, known resources, etc., rather than with the enforcement of established long-term programs. A wise Authority will try to maintain an unallocated water reserve, diversity sources and supply, and develop local storage, possibly underground, against drought periods. These and other matters call for foresight and flexibility. Indeed, the maintenance of a wise water policy is more an art than a science—an art which should be acquired by all water-short countries.

Guidance in the development of such policies as well as specific projects is available to the developing countries. A variety of U.N. agencies—the Food and Agricultural Organization, the U.N. Economic and Cultural Commission, the International Atomic Energy Agency (IAEA), and the World Meteorological Organization, can all provide technical as-

sistance and some financial support. Additional monies may
be available through the U.N. Special Funds. The U.S.
Agency for International Development provides technical assistance in developing water resources and is currently, in
cooperation with the Office of Saline Water, developing guidance materials on desalting plants and their costs. (One publication, on solar stills, is already available.) The Office of
Saline Water is authorized by Congress to provide technical
assistance to countries interested in desalination; extensive
desalination feasibility studies or projects have been or are
being carried out by OSW personnel in conjunction with
experts from Mexico, Greece, Israel, and Saudi Arabia. Other
teams of technical experts from such diverse countries as Germany, Great Britain, Poland, and Israel have provided assistance to water planners in other nations.

No Ready-made Recipes

But how does one utilize such guidance? How can an effective water program be organized in view of the many
problems, limitations, and conflicts that exist? It takes a
brave man, or at least one who has done it the hard way, to
offer an answer. Such a man is Aharon Wiener, Director General of Tahal—Water Planning for Israel, Ltd. It is a mark
of Wiener's achievements in the water-planning field that,
when he spoke at the International Conference on Water for
Peace in late May, 1967, delegates from Arab nations, whose
troops were then massed on Israel's borders, attended the
meetings he addressed, and at least one representative of the
United Arab Republic took extensive notes on Wiener's comments at a small, informal session. In the next chapter, Israel's water-supply plan will be described in some detail;
here, it is sufficient to say that it involves everything from desalination and sewage reclamation to utilization of the River
Jordan and underground water supplies, and it has built into

it extreme conservation techniques in domestic, agricultural, and industrial use.

Yet Wiener, a wise man in water planning, says bluntly that no ready-made recipes exist. Carrying this theme one step further, he adds that any nation's organizational plan is determined by the nature of the development program itself and in accord with sociopolitical and sociopsychological context rather than classic organization theories.

In his formal address, he said:

> The principal goal for the organization of national water resources planning should be the establishment of an organization structure capable—as it were spontaneously—of producing effective programs, and of developing the capacity to implement them. This—rather than the sophistication of organizational formal structures—is the crux of the matter. Such an organization should encompass all of the political and social goals of the water supply program, and all the organizational elements involved in achieving those goals so that there is a minimum of fragmentation in establishing overall goals and means for carrying them out.

The developing countries, he added, require a more comprehensive planning framework than that of the more developed countries because such countries are dealing with many of the issues faced by the more developed countries as well as with problems unique to their own situations. Also, undeveloped countries, without traditional frameworks for planned or spontaneous change, require more public intervention to effect changes in the allocation of material and nonmaterial resources. But the creation of organizational patterns best suited to the national water needs is generally easier in a developing country because what organizational structure does exist is relatively new and has not become so firmly entrenched and resistant to change that powerful political force is required to move it.

Discussing the "success requirements" for the organization

of national water-resource planning, he called first for a demarcation between planning of water resources and planning of other sectors of the economy, although noting it should be kept in mind that the volume and rate of water-resource development will be controlled by over-all economic-development programs, whose goals include increasing the volume of production to increase national and per-capita income; modifying social and geographical distribution of income; improving other economic factors such as employment, balance of payments, ability to save, and the like; and achieving these objectives within the existing political decision-making processes and the prevailing political and economic ideology in a given country.

The latter point is of major importance because it relates to the financing and control of water-development programs such as the use of desalting plants, and it encompasses such factors as a nation's attitudes toward ownership of the means of production and tolerance of state intervention. The U.N. survey *Water Desalination in Developing Countries,* published in 1964, showed that about 70 per cent of the installed desalting capacity in the developing countries at that time was government-owned; the trend since has been even more overwhelmingly in that direction. Hence, a nation's policy toward government intervention in matters of economic development has a direct bearing on the use of desalination technology, for the government makes the decisions and determines the priorities and methods of achieving national economic objectives.

Wiener warned, however, of letting the obvious and important interrelationship between water-resource development and over-all economic development lead to the creation of a planning organization of such "dinosaurian" size that "excessive numbers of hierarchic levels . . . would vitiate or even nullify its planning endeavors." What is required, he said, is an over-all coordinating group and other groups with responsibilities for various areas of economic development. However, he cautioned:

> Even a properly set up subsystem will still require for its effective operation a great amount of two-way interaction with the rest of the economy. . . . The boundaries between the water resources subsystem and the rest of the economy should be determined in a way that would ensure the inclusion within the direct or coordinative control of the subsystem of the six main inputs . . . major capital investments, supporting capital investments and current production inputs . . . transformation inputs, these being the inputs required to improve know-how and techniques, to modify psychological space, and to restructure institutional space.

He added:

> Exclusive control over any one of these inputs by an agency not bearing direct responsibility for the main program objectives will lead to excess growth . . . of some aspects of the program and to a subnormal growth . . . of others. This will, in our context of water resources development, cause more damage than in other developmental contexts, because a kind of negative feedback process usually develops here which tends to strengthen the more vigorous arms and weaken the inactive. Usually, the major capital investment spheres will be overextended, while most other essential input fields will usually be characterized by sub-normal growth, or even stagnancy. The net effect of so unbalanced a water program will be that scarce resources will be absorbed with little prospect of fruition, leading, as in a vicious circle, to more unproductive investments.

Wiener then posed the question of national planning versus local or regional planning. The greater the scarcity of capital and of human and social resources, the less a nation can afford the loss to the economy which results from patchy planning. Influences favoring adoption of national solutions include the disparity of resources between regions, short distances between the resource groups intended for development, high rate of development, high exploitation of resources, availability of trained manpower and, on the political side, "the necessity to project an image of creative national development thinking." It may also, he admitted, "be convenient to have an alibi to postpone development action until over-all national programs can be drawn up. . . . Fierce competition for human and material resources between various subsystems will be encountered in development programs in emerging economies," he warned with experienced realism, and said that competition would extend to various phases of the program, such as data collection, data evaluation, long-term planning, short-term planning, and the like.

> Under the prevailing type of organization for water resource programs, the responsibility for creation of the various inputs will be located in a number of independent agencies. These agencies compete for limited resources without being in a position to judge true priorities or to reconcile conflicting claims. . . . More aggressive units . . . will grab more than their share and, therefore, move ahead faster than other . . . units. The former units will thus hold positions of strength when resources are next allocated; they will also exert an attraction on the best professional manpower, thereby impoverishing the stock of human resources of other units or agencies that most need them.

The most effective use of desalination technology can only result from the application of such principles and the avoidance of such pitfalls as the several experts quoted in these pages emphasize. For the developing countries, desalting is not a miraculous panacea but a tool for expanding water resources and improving the economy within an over-all resources plan. In some few nations, like Kuwait, it may provide the principal water resource; in others, such as Mexico, Israel, Saudi Arabia, and Venezuela, it will be an important supplement. Desalting may help make possible extensive expansion of agriculture, either by providing fresh water directly for irrigation or by reducing—through blending with existing supplies—the salinity of far greater amounts of water than the desalting plant itself will produce. It may be used to improve living standards within big cities and to permit urban growth. It may make possible the development of industries and seaports in given locations. It may be used to exploit existing water that would otherwise be unusable—from rivers that have become too salty or polluted or underground resources that are overmineralized.

How desalination is being specifically utilized for these purposes today in the developing countries is the subject of the next chapter.

6

Desalting in the Developing Countries—Some Specifics

The 1964 U.N. report on desalting in developing countries underscores all of the statements in the last chapter about the need for comprehensive and intelligent water planning, for it presents an almost psychedelic pattern of varying costs, practices, applications, and viewpoints. Although limited in its approach, the study is the most extensive of its kind and presents a strong case for the future of desalting technology.

United Nations Under-Secretary for Economic and Social Affairs Philippe De Seynes set the tone for the report in the introduction, saying, "in recent years, interest in desalination has grown greatly as it becomes apparent that, even in countries well endowed with water resources, severe regional problems of balancing water supply and water requirements will arise within the near future. Water desalination is of particularly great potential significance for the arid countries whose development is being impeded by inadequate or unreliable water supplies."

The U.N. report had three main purposes: to determine which water-short areas with economic growth potential in developing countries appeared to have possibilities for the economic use of desalted water; to collect technical and economic data on principal plants in operation; and to make available costs, prices, and utilization patterns of desalted water from conventional sources of electricity in water-short areas.

Unfortunately, it is valuable today mostly as a starting point from which to look at the developing countries. The survey is limited in that it pays little heed to agricultural use of desalted water—reasonably enough, since, up to 1962, the end of the period it covers, desalted water had proved too costly for irrigation use. Moreover, the U.N. investigators put an arbitrary limit on the distance to which they considered it economically feasible to transport desalinated water—fifty miles horizontally and slightly less than 500 yards vertically. These limits are mentioned because they place obvious restrictions on the conclusions the investigators could reach. Elsewhere in this book, for example, it has been noted that fresh water is being moved nearly 700 miles in California and long distances in New York State, and that present schemes call for moving fresh water from the Colorado River hundreds of miles to central Arizona. The arbitrary water-transport distances established by the U. N. people are unrealistic, for in many parts of the world it is now necessary to transport reservoir or other water much farther than fifty miles across the ground and much higher than 500 yards to make it available. In many future situations, it will be less costly to pipe desalted water 100 miles than to pipe alternative river or reservoir or underground water two or three or seven times that distance. The cost of moving conventional surface water longer distances is cheaper than moving desalted water shorter distances only if the former can flow downward, impelled by gravity, and if the desalted water has to be pumped uphill for a considerable stretch. Generally, this would not be the case in coastal desert areas. Hence, the United Nations' findings are reported here as minimal rather than maximal.

It should also be noted that the report was completed some time before advances in desalting technology had led to predicted cost factors well below those considered realistic in 1962.

The United Nations invited seventy-four countries and territories to participate in the survey. Lack of available information finally limited the study to forty-three nations or territories, of which only eighteen were at the time using desalinated water. The prices of converted salt water varied as widely as the cost of fresh water, proving, if anything, that in no two developing countries are water-planning problems exactly the same. Patterns of water use were as divergent.

At the time of the study, desalination technology was being used to some extent in Mauritania, South Africa, South West Africa, Tunisia, the United Arab Republic, Bahrein, Iran, Israel, Kuwait, Qatar, Saudi Arabia, the Bahamas, Bermuda, Ecuador, the Netherlands Antilles, Peru, the Virgin Islands, and on Guernsey in the Channel Islands of Great Britain. Additional desalination plants were planned, approved, or under construction in the Canary Islands, Libya, Tunisia, Israel, Kuwait, Qatar, Saudi Arabia, Bermuda, Chile, the Netherlands Antilles, Venezuela, the Virgin Islands, and Malta. The Office of Saline Water's 1966 Annual Report shows additional installations planned or already on stream in these and other developing countries.

Most of the plants operating in 1962 were either distillation units using flash evaporation or submerged-tube methods or else electrodialysis units. There were three vapor compression units. Only one, at Guernsey, utilized the multistage flash process. The electrodialysis units took feed water ranging up to 31,000 parts of salt per million and produced water with 500 PPM dissolved salts. The distillation units, dealing primarily with sea water, produced fresh water with as low as 2 PPM dissolved salts. Their operators included

military bases, hospitals, hotels, oil companies and other industries, and government agencies. Fuels used included coal,
diesel and fuel oil, natural gas, and hydroelectric power. To
these, the future will add nuclear power.

What the U.N. Study Predicted

Of particular interest is a section of the U.N. report offer-
ing a perspective for the wider application of water desalination in specific areas. Even though agricultural uses are not
generally considered, there is a striking variety of other uses
in the geographically broad list of possibilities seen at the
end of 1962. Among them:

Ethiopia. Port development and the establishment of a refinery appeared to make water desalination essential to provide water for industry and households near and in Assab.

Mali. Desalination feasibility was dependent on hydrological studies and industrial development plans, but desalting, it was thought, could provide water for industry and
mining in the Guondam area.

South Africa. Utilization of desalination for mining, households, and cattle watering was dependent on the amount of
brackish water to be removed from mines and on experiments under way on the electrodialysis process for agricultural uses.

Mauritania. Use of desalination for households, shipping,
and tourism in Port Étienne was dependent on decisions gov-
erning construction of a new pipeline to Port Étienne.

United Arab Republic. Desalting appeared possible for
mining and industry in the Red Sea region but was dependent on a hydrological survey and on a comparative study of
desalination and a long-distance pipeline from the Nile to
the coast. At the time of the study, there were U.A.R. desalting
plants in use at several phosphate plants and zinc mines.

(Later, a 600,000-gallons-per-day multistage flash distillation plant was built in the Sinai desert and two smaller plants just south of Cairo.)

India. Dependent on economic feasibility studies for the first three locations and on prospects for desalination of brackish water at the fourth, desalting was considered a way to provide water for households, shipping, fishing, and industry at Madras, Calcutta, Kandla, and Ernakulam Inlet in Kerala.

Israel. Desalination plants were already under construction to provide water for households, industry, and shipping at the Gulf of Aqaba port of Eilat.

Qatar. It was thought probable that additional desalination plants would be required in the near future to provide household water at Doha. (By 1967, Qatar was operating five plants at Doha, with a total rated capacity at least nine times that which existed in 1962. An additional plant is being constructed at this writing.)

Saudi Arabia. Desalination of brackish water in the Eastern Province could, it was believed, provide water for households and industry; a hydrological survey was required before plans could be made to augment the water supplies for the city of Jedda. (Since then, extensive water-resource development, including desalination, has begun.)

Turkey. Economic analysis was required to determine the feasibility of desalting water for use in households, industry, and irrigation in the Lake Hazar and Gallipoli Peninsula areas.

Greece. Small desalination plants appeared attractive as a means of solving serious water-supply problems on the Greek islands for household and tourist use. (As noted earlier, much of this has already been accomplished.)

Malta. Desalting appeared to be the only economic solution for tourist development. (Plant construction has since been undertaken.)

Ecuador. A comparative cost analysis between the use of desalination and a Daule River development project to provide water for tourism and households on the Santa Elena Peninsula was recommended as warranted. (Desalting plants have since been built at some points on the Peninsula.)

Mexico. Desalination seemed a long-term possibility for future development of tourism in the Cozumel and Carmen areas and an economic alternative to the water-supply problems in Tijuana in the Mexican state of Baja California. (See Chapter 4 for details of the Tijuana story.)

Netherlands Antilles. Expansion of existing desalting plants seemed probable to meet growing needs of households, tourism, and other industry. (Such expansion has been taking place.)

Venezuela. Development of desalting to promote tourism around Puerto Píritu and the island of Margarita was dependent on economic feasibility studies.

Where desalination was being used or planned, it was envisaged either as a principal source of water supply or as part of a supply network, indicating the flexibility of the technology's role in developing countries. Desalination plants installed prior to completion of recommended inventories of existing brackish- and fresh-water reserves, the U.N. report noted, may become less important if large water sources are subsequently located, but—again the emphasis is on flexibility—they can be dismantled and moved to another water-short location. Even if a plant should be discarded, the report stated, it may have "justified its installation through its development stimulus to the area."

The United Nations strongly urged comprehensive water-supply surveys. Such surveys include both technical and economic information on water resources and comparative costs involved in utilizing desalting or other sources. In those areas where there does not appear to be a feasible alternative to desalination, such cost studies relate largely to the size of the plant and the process to be used, taking into account short-, medium-, and long-range requirements. Where desalting plants are already operating and more water is needed, the studies must take into account comparisons between adding additional desalting modules or plants and developing other water resources.

One feature of the U.N. report was a special look at the problem of ground-water overpumping. Ground waters represent the largest potential untapped water resources outside of the oceans themselves. Where salt-water encroachment problems have been caused by overpumping, a desalting plant can add to the local water supply and allow control of pumping to conserve ground water.

Some of the report's important conclusions were that (1) desalination makes possible the gradual expansion of a supply system on the basis of step-by-step installation of plant capacity, whereas other alternatives may require construction of a costly reservoir or pipeline with a large capital investment in capacity perhaps not used for decades; (2) desalination provides a quick supply of fresh water when it must be acquired immediately before other sources can be developed later, and the plant can be used on a stand-by basis in time of drought or to meet peak-load demands; and (3) perhaps most important of all, when desalination technology is employed, there are no conflicts over traditional water rights between communities, states, or nations sharing the same source.

Predicting improved technology, a lowering of desalting costs with conventional water-supply costs rising simultaneously in the face of increased demands, and a rise in per-capita income in developing nations enabling people to pay more for water, the U.N. report foresaw "a steady expansion in demand for desalinated water in water-short areas. . . . For such potentially water-short areas, desalination gives some assurance that fresh water will continue to be available in the future, provided it can be economically justified and that such areas are within a reasonable distance from the sea or an inland brackish water body."

As predicted, in the five years since the U.N. study was made, desalination technology has become an increasingly important factor in water-supply planning, and the United Nations itself is intensifying its work in the field by undertaking studies in relation to the application of desalting techniques in developing countries. One is a study of methods for determining and forecasting water demand, with particular emphasis on the elasticity of demand in response to changes in price and quality. Both relate directly to desalination use. Another study will focus on the use of local energy sources for desalting, including the use of geothermal and oil-shale energy and the burning of refuse. The third study will focus on foreign-exchange aspects of different desalting processes, including the effect of use of local construction materials.

The United Nations will also finance desalting projects from its Special Fund. One such project is assistance to Israel on an electrodialysis demonstration plant at Mashavei Sadeh.

During 1966, desalting plants were completed in Iran, Israel, Kuwait, Bermuda, Ecuador, the Virgin Islands, Peru, Italy, Malta, Portugal, Spain, the United Kingdom, and Australia. They had a total capacity of 11,075,000 gallons of fresh water daily. Approved or under construction during the same year were additional plants in Libya, Mauritania, Tunisia, Kuwait, Oman, Saudi Arabia, Antigua, Bermuda, West Germany, Greece, Spain, the Spanish Sahara, the Soviet Union, the United States, and Australia. These plants range in size from the 150-MGD plant near Los Angeles to small solar distillation units. Their total capacity is 203,683,800 gallons per day. Already planned, at the end of 1966, were other plants in the United Arab Republic, Israel, Saudi Arabia, Brazil, the Virgin Islands, Mexico, Italy, Spain, and Australia, with an additional capacity of 147,347,000 gallons per day.

But such statistically impressive recapitulations give only a superficial indication of the role desalination is playing in the world today—and especially in the developing countries. One way to get behind the statistics is to look at some specific countries where desalination already is or shortly will be a significant factor in national or regional water planning.

Kuwait—Dhows to Multistage Flash Distillation

Kuwait is a very special case of applied desalination. Most of its water comes from desalting plants. Israel and Saudi Arabia are notable examples of the relationship of desalination to total water planning. Mexico, where desalting will supplement other water resources on a more localized basis, also envisions the possibility of broad, long-range use of desalination technology. But the tiny oil-rich sheikdom of Kuwait might be described as a showcase filled with a working-model history of modern desalination technology.

At the end of 1966, some twenty desalting plants with a capacity of more than 24 MGD of fresh water were operating or under construction in Kuwait. Since then, the government has contracted for the construction of two 4-MGD plants and is preparing to build another plant—associated with what will be the largest electric power plant in the Middle East—which will produce between 14 and 20 MGD of fresh water. The new construction will more than double the amount of fresh water being produced by desalination in this small nation, whose total land area is less than 6,000 square miles.

Twenty-five years ago, Kuwait had a population of about 60,000 people. Its main claim to fame was that the city of Kuwait, on Kuwait Bay, off the Persian Gulf, had been selected as the seaport terminal of the Berlin-to-Baghdad railroad. Its main exports at the time were horses, wool, dates, and pearls, traded largely with India, Iraq, Iran, and the Arabian coast. Prior to 1925, the inhabitants relied entirely on water from shallow wells, which produced limited quantities of drinkable water. From 1925 to 1950, water was brought by sailing dhows to three large reservoirs, where the silt was allowed to settle before the water was distributed in cans to the people. Because the boats were at the mercy of gales and sandstorms, the water supply was unreliable. It was also of poor quality. Another source of water was the small amount of rainfall, which filled individual wells and artesian wells that produced brackish water with a high salinity.

Oil was discovered in Kuwait in 1938 and first exported in 1946. Since then, the petroleum industry has made Kuwait the world's second largest exporter and fourth largest producer of crude oil. It provides 98 per cent of the country's income. The population has risen to more than 468,000, more than half of whom are from other Arab nations and who work in the oil fields and the Kuwaiti civil service. Kuwait has used its enormous income to create a welfare state, which guarantees free medical care, education, and social security to the entire population. It also provides a growing amount of fresh water, to meet needs that between 1953 and 1959 alone increased tenfold.

With the flow of oil creating new industrial complexes and a growing population, Sheikh Abdullah al-Salim al-Sabah, the ruler of Kuwait, in 1953 took the first step to produce the water needed for both municipal and industrial use. He commissioned the construction of a 1.2-MGD submerged-tube evaporator plant at Shuwaikh on Kuwait Bay, where it began producing fresh water from sea water containing 48,200 PPM of total dissolved solids.

Prosaically named Shuwaikh A, the plant was the first in a long line—soon to reach Shuwaikh G with the completion of a plant with a capacity four times that of the initial unit. After the first two submerged-tube evaporators were built, Kuwait began purchasing the then new multistage flash evaporators, four of which, including "G," will be on stream at Shuwaikh. By 1965, when Shuwaikh F, was commissioned, the water demand had grown to the point where additional multistage flash plants were being built across Kuwait Bay at Shuaiba on the Persian Gulf. Shuaiba A, commissioned in 1965, had a capacity of 3.6 MGD; Shuaiba B will add another 2.4 MGD.

During the same period in which desalination became a major source for the nation, ground water with a reasonable salinity was discovered at Raudhatain, about sixty-five miles from Kuwait City. But the field was not as plentiful as had at first been thought. Also, the number of wells dug was much greater than had been planned for, with the result that the salinity of the ground water rose to 1,000 PPM because of overuse.

One other major water resource in Kuwait is a brackish water field at Silibiyah, which produces water with 4,000 PPM total dissolved solids. Blended with desalted water, this field now augments the total water supply by producing more than 16 MGD.

Oil companies in Kuwait, building their own desalting plants, have further increased the country's water supply, and a smaller, 240,000-gallons-per-day electrodialysis plant has been built at the Kuwait airport for use in desalting brackish underground water.

Originally, the desalted water was distributed by truck, but now is piped to houses in Kuwait City. Until the pipes were installed, the cost of distribution almost equaled the cost of desalination. One unusual factor involved in Kuwait's massive use of desalting technology for water supply is the availability of natural gas, a by-product of the oil industry, to provide free energy fuel for the desalting and electric power plants.

Saudi Arabia—Nation Without a River

Saudi Arabia is one of Kuwait's neighbors. Occupying four-fifths of the Arabian peninsula, with the Red Sea on most of its west coast and the Persian Gulf on the east, Saudi Arabia is 150 times the size of Kuwait, and has seventeen times the population.

A shortage of water is one of the most important factors slowing down the economic and social development of this largely desert nation. It is the largest nation in the world without a single river. Its arid wastelands slope barren and uncultivated from 9,000-foot heights in the west to the shores of the Persian Gulf. The U.N. surveyors in 1962 estimated that less than 1 per cent of Saudi Arabia's land area was being farmed. The country depends heavily on imports to meet its food requirements, although it does produce dates, wheat, barley, fruit, hides, and wool, and raises some camels, horses, donkeys, and sheep. To a limited extent, Saudi Arabia exports hides, wool, and gum.

Oil is the keystone of the modern Saudi Arabian economy, as it is in Kuwait. The country sits above the second largest oil reserve in the Middle East and produces about 7 per cent of the world's oil supply. Recently, gold, silver, and rich iron ore have been discovered.

Oddly, one small part of Saudi Arabia in the southwest has a flood-control problem caused by torrential monsoon rains, which create flash floods that rampage through the normally dry Wadi Jizan east of the Red Sea and north of the Yemen border. But Saudi Arabia as a whole averages less than four inches of rainfall annually, literally a drop in the bucket when it comes to replenishing the extensive underground water resources that underlie large sections of the desert.

With its oil income, and technical assistance from the Food and Agricultural Organization of the United Nations, the

U.N. Special Fund, and the Office of Saline Water of the U.S. Department of the Interior, Saudi Arabia has launched a major effort to use all possible means of providing the additional water resources that the U.N. study termed "the key to Saudi Arabia's future economic development." Agriculture and Water Minister, His Excellency H. E. Mishari explained the philosophy underlying his government's water development policy in the preamble to one of the Ministry's resource surveys:

> The government desires to improve the living standards of rural people within the kingdom through the investigation and development of soil, native vegetation, surface and subsurface water resources and the development of effective production, marketing, financing and serving facilities to assure livestock growers and farmers a fair price for their increased production.

This, however, tells just a small part of the story, which already involves an investment of $146 million in fresh-water resource exploration and development. Goals of this intensive program are to provide water first, for domestic use; second, for industry and industrial expansion; and third, for the irrigation and agricultural development of as large an area as possible.

The Ministry of Agriculture and Water has launched an ambitious educational program to train Saudi Arabian water technicians to work with international experts and consultants. For the seven-year period ending in 1967, a total of $196 million was allocated for development work, all but $50 million of it for water projects. These projects range from extensive surveys of ground-water resources, to flood control in the southwest, to extensive use of desalination, which is particularly economical for use along the extensive coastlines. It will also be used for demineralizing brackish ground waters from the deep underground aquifers as well as other ground waters affected by oil-field brines and sea-water intrusion. Ample resources of gas and oil to fuel desalting plants make the new technology particularly advantageous as a water resource in Saudi Arabia.

Six major water development efforts are currently under way.

At the Qatif oasis on the east coast, the artesian flow is being brought under control and a drainage system installed. Qatif is an ancient Phoenician city and one of the most famous agricultural areas in the kingdom, but its rich water resources have been demeaned by lack of drainage and water control, which has led to deterioration of soil productivity because of increased water-logging and salinity. The Arabian Oil Company cooperated with the government in studies leading to the development of a plan that includes drilling fifty-two high production wells, eliminating all excessive and defective wells and improving nineteen existing wells, and constructing a modern irrigation and drainage system.

Another noted agricultural area, al-Hasa, in the Eastern Province, is also being revitalized. This famed date-producing area and oasis for caravans moving across ancient trade routes has also suffered deterioration of soil productivity because of increasing salinity. The largest agricultural development project in the kingdom, the al-Hasa work will benefit 190,000 residents of forty villages. It includes drainage construction to send water to add another fifteen miles to the agricultural areas, well control, a unified irrigation system, reclamation of the saline area, and scientific agricultural expansion.

Also in the east, the Faisal Settlement Project will irrigate acres of desert land to provide permanent, productive home sites for 10,000 nomadic Bedouins. Some fifty new wells will be drilled to make this possible.

In Tihama, a major flood-control dam and the upgrading of indigenous irrigation systems using flood waters will improve the life and income of farmers in the area.

Ground-water development for municipal, village, and stock-watering supplies has been undertaken throughout the kingdom, but the biggest such project by far is in cooperation with the municipal government of Riyadh, the Saudi Arabian capital. This rapidly growing city has been hampered by water shortages, which inhibit its industrial and municipal expansion. To alleviate this problem, a broad-scale development project includes the construction of cooling, treatment, and pumping plants, water reservoirs, and distribution systems. Some of the new wells bring water from sources as much as 1,500 meters below the surface (three times the height the United Nations study called economically practical in 1962).

The sixth major water-supply undertaking is desalination. In what Prince Mohamed Al Faisal, Director of Sea Water Desalination in the Ministry of Agriculture and Water, calls an "emergency program," Saudi Arabia by 1970 will have invested approximately $40 million to supplement the water supply of key coastal areas.

The largest plant already in the equipment fabrication state is a 5-MGD unit, which will be part of a dual-purpose operation at Jedda, the country's main Red Sea port. When completed, it will also provide fifty megawatts of net exportable electricity, and will ultimately be expanded to produce four times as much fresh water. When the plant is completed, Jedda will no longer be dependent on inadequate water supplies piped in from Wadi Fatma, and that water will become largely available for agricultural use.

In 1962, the United Nations noted that "the present water supply in Jedda is inadequate to satisfy the domestic requirements of the increasing population and the additional needs of the large numbers of pilgrims," tens of thousands of whom pass through Jedda annually on their way to the holy city of Mecca. Although in 1962 water shortages had not affected industrial development in the Jedda area, the United Nations said, "this may . . . become a serious problem," noting, in addition, that "the expansion of farming in the area . . . is already hindered by the lack of adequate water."

The Jedda desalting plant, then, will serve both people and industry, while at the same time releasing the Wadi Fatma water to the farmers. Although this plant—being built with technical assistance from the OSW—is not expected to be on stream until 1969, two smaller 61,000-gallons-per-day plants are being completed at points north of Jedda, where they will provide emergency water supplies for two towns where drought caused a sudden drying-up of natural water supplies, and where, as a result, water is being rationed at a rate of one gallon per person daily. They are being designed so they can be moved, if necessary, to other locations where similar emergencies develop.

Other similar plants are scheduled for completion in 1968, at Safaniya, an oil community where water is needed for the oil-field workers and their families, and another with a 150,000-gallons-per-day capacity at Al-Khafji in the Eastern Province. These are all in addition to plants already operating at Dhahran, Abqaiq, and Ras Tanura, the largest of which has a 700,000-gallons-per-day capacity while the others range from 50,000-gallons-per-day upward.

One other major "emergency" plan is now in the feasibility testing stage. It involves a large desalter, which will provide a regional fresh-water supply for Ras Tanura, Dammam, Dhahran, Al-Khobar, and Qatif. When on stream, it will provide between 8 and 12 MGD, as compared to the presently existing total capacity of about 2 MGD in the entire kingdom.

In addition to the emergency program, Prince Faisal's office has short-range goals, which include the use of the present technology to develop new water sources and to supplement existing natural resources by blending with brackish water. From a long-range viewpoint, he hopes to develop the sea as a major source of potable water and as a reservoir. He also expects to develop and implement programs to advance the technology of desalination through applied research, and he hopes to see desalted water replacing, wherever possible, natural sources as the main water supply for cities, towns, and industry, so that natural water can be used almost exclusively for agriculture.

Israel—Survival Water Supplies

Across the Gulf of Aqaba from Saudi Arabia is Israel. This new nation, in existence only since 1948, when it was created by the United Nations, is one of the water-planning show-cases of the world and may become the first nation in the Middle East to utilize nuclear power for the production of fresh water from the Mediterranean Sea. Like other nations in that part of the world, Israel's survival and future growth will depend in large measure on the country's ability to increase the amount of water available for domestic, industrial, and agricultural use.

This fact was bluntly stated in the U.N. survey, which said: "The salient aspect of the economy of Israel is that water, not land, is the limiting factor in the country's development. Because of the rapidly increasing demand for water, the country is compelled to seek an effective and fast way of augmenting its limited resources of fresh water."

Israel's water problems, in a sense, are capsule versions of the water-supply exigencies facing many new nations in the world today. Israel's moment of decision may come in the mid-1970's, for this tiny nation is already utilizing more than 90 per cent of all existing water resources and can look only to desalination as a known means of providing a significant amount of the additional water needed by then (unless ultimately more Jordan River water is made available).

Although a relatively sophisticated nation, culturally, industrially, and economically, Israel classifies as a developing nation, largely because of the accident of history that created the new state in the arid Middle East only two decades ago.

At the time Israel became a sovereign state, it had a population of 915,000; by 1964, as a result of a policy of open immigration, the population had reached 2,430,000. And, by 1970, it is predicted that the figure will pass 3 million. (These figures are based on the Israeli boundaries that preceded the Arab-Israeli war in 1967. Any territorial and population changes that may become permanent as the result of the conflict will alter the water-supply context within which this is written.)

Israel's total prewar land area was about 8,000 square miles, bordering on the Mediterranean Sea, Lebanon, Jordan, the United Arab Republic, and the Gulf of Aqaba. Most of the population is located in the Mediterranean coastal plains, although the growing commercial and fishing port of Eilat is at Israel's southern tip, on the Gulf of Aqaba. The climate in the northern part of Israel, where the industrial plants and the many major citrus plantations are located, is mild, typical of the eastern Mediterranean, whereas the southern part of the country, comprising the Negev and the Arava, is largely arid desert. The country's major river, the Jordan, represents about 31 per cent of the total available fresh water. Annual rainfall ranges from 20 inches along the Mediterranean coast and 24–30 inches in the eastern mountains to about 8 inches at Beersheba, farther south, and dips to 1–2 inches in the southern desert regions and Eilat.

Although vestiges of amazingly well-engineered water-supply systems dating back into antiquity have been found by archaeologists digging in the Palestinian mountains and hills, modern water systems in the area prior to the establishment of the Israeli nation in 1948 were generally local and based largely on ground water or the use of river-flow during the summer months. Comprehensive planning started only after 1948 and led to the development of a master plan drawn up in 1950. Progress was slow, but in 1953, Israel began the development of regional projects to move water from areas of surplus to areas of shortage. These projects were almost all completed by 1958. Then, work began on the Lake Tiberias-Negev project. A series of conduits move water fed by the Jordan River and underground springs into Lake Tiberias (also known as the Sea of Galilee and Yam Kinneret) then north and west to Haifa and Acre and south toward the arid desert areas.

More than three-fourths of Israel's water resources are in the northern part of the country, while more than half of the arable lands are in the south. The proven fresh-water resources that can be developed by 1975 are estimated capable of providing 1,540 million cubic meters of water annually, and an additional 100 million cubic meters of water may be available from other sources. Of the already proven resources, more than half is ground water—although this source is increasingly plagued by salinity problems—and 31 per cent is river water, largely from the Jordan. An additional 5 per cent comes from intermittent winter floods and 9 per cent from reclaimed sewage. Total water consumption by 1962 had reached 1,223 million cubic meters, about one-fourth of which came from overpumped ground-water resources. This overpumping, coupled with five years of comparative drought, has resulted in lower water tables and sea-water encroachment in underground coastal aquifers near Haifa and Tel Aviv. Israeli water planners recognize that the overpumping will have to stop before the end of the present decade, and that the water will have to be replaced if the nation is to have a stable water supply.

The present status of Israel's water problems was summarized by Vice-Chairman I. Vilentchuk of the Israel Sea Water Conversion Commission (formed in 1959 to explore the possibilities of desalting as a source of water for Israel) at the International Conference on Water for Peace, in May, 1967. At that time, actual water consumption, including loss in transit, had reached close to 90 per cent of the estimated

1975 capacity of 1.5 million cubic meters per year mentioned earlier. Israel was using about 1 billion gallons of water daily. He said:

> Owing to this high degree of exploitation, water has become the only rationed commodity in Israel. Since not all water resources are as yet fully developed, heavy overpumping of wells, mainly in the Mediterranean coastal zone, has taken place, thus exposing the aquifer to sea water encroachment.
>
> It is considered of paramount necessity to put an end to this overpumping . . . and, during the seventies, to restore gradually the underground waters to their desired level. . . . The salinity of Israel's water is another cause for grave concern. A sizable portion of the country's natural waters is of a salinity which is somewhat higher than is permissible for irrigating salt-sensitive crops, such as citrus, which is the largest single item of the country's agricultural export.

It is predicted that, by 1980, agriculture, now using 80 per cent of Israel's water supply, will use 1.145 million cubic meters of water annually, that industry will use 220 million cubic meters, and that municipal consumption will reach 400 million cubic meters. This is 1.765 million cubic meters annually—more than 100 million gallons of water over the amount estimated to be available for daily use in the entire country by 1975. Unless new waters are found—probably from desalination—Israel faces not a 34 per cent increase in agricultural production as officials first predicted, but a sharp cutback in output with a resultant blow to the economy of the nation.

How important does desalination loom in Israel's future? In March, 1966, Aharon Wiener, the director of Tahal, Israel's water-planning agency, said in a *Jerusalem Post* interview:

> Everyone agrees that we will have to turn to desalination sooner or later. There is no ultimate choice. The only question is which is it to be—sooner or later. If we have good rains, we can postpone the need. But I cannot advise the Government to

take the risk, to gamble on rain. Our Board of Review, which includes some of the best men in the world, like Abel Wolman, Raymond Hill and Phillip Sporn, all agree that our reserves are too low to take any chances.

Since the appointment of the Sea Water Conversion Commission in 1959, Israel has become extremely active in the desalting field. Among the physical and economic conditions favorable to the development of desalination are the length of the Mediterranean coastline, the relatively short distances involved in conveying desalted water overland, and the country-wide power and water grids, which simplify utilization of both electrical and water outputs from new dual-purpose plants.

In 1964, a joint United States–Israel team was appointed by President Johnson and Israeli Prime Minister Levi Eshkol to study the potentials of large-scale, nuclear-powered desalination technology for Israel. In October of that year, the team published a report recommending a 100-MGD dual-purpose plant on the Mediterranean coast, south of Tel Aviv. This multistage flash plant would be powered by a nuclear reactor and would provide 200 megawatts of electricity in addition to the sweet water. Subsequently, Kaiser Engineers and the Catalytic Construction Company undertook a study and confirmed the technical and economic feasibility of the project.

Initially, it was projected that the ultimate cost of water would be slightly under 30 cents per thousand gallons. Since then, a revised study, based on the production of 300 megawatts of electricity, brought the price down to about 24-26 cents per thousand gallons. This is comparable with prices in many U.S. communities, but still considerably higher than prices paid by farmers in Israel or elsewhere. According to one Israeli spokesman, however, the price could be tolerated for use in producing high-income citrus crops, and, moreover, "we have to have the water no matter what the cost."

Although land is being set aside for the plant at Ashdod, on the Mediterranean, details of the financing still have to be worked out, and construction is being delayed pending studies of the actual functioning of the new OSW plant at San Diego, California. The San Diego plant is testing components, which will be used in both the big 150-MGD plant planned by the Metropolitan Water District in Los Angeles, and the Israeli plant at Ashdod. Unfortunately, Israel cannot wait too long for either financing or technological improvements. The deadline of the early 1970's is still there and made stricter by the possibility of having to supply water to raise the living standards of people living in recently occupied territories of the Gaza Strip, the Sinai Desert, and West Jordan. No final decisions had been reached at this writing, but necessary geologic surveys had been completed and an oceanographic survey was under way.

Smaller desalination units have been on stream in Israel for some time. As early as 1957, an ion-exchange plant was built at Elath by the Ministry of Development and was operated by the Mekoroth Water Company, Ltd., Israel's nonprofit water utility. It was used to process brackish water from the Yotvata wells for distribution, primarily to children in the area who often suffered after drinking well water with a high magnesium sulphate content. In 1961, an electrodialysis plant was built at Sdom by the Negev Institute for Arid Zone Research to supply drinking water for that small agricultural settlement.

The extreme shortage of water resources in southern Negev has given that area a high priority for desalting plant construction. Two plants have been built at the port city of Eilat. One, a 1-MGD unit, has been exceeding its design capacity by about 8 per cent in spite of the extremely high salinity of the Red Sea waters—45,000 PPM, as compared to average sea-water levels of 35,000 PPM. The fresh water is mixed with well water and supplies half the water needs of the town's 10,000 year-round residents and the tens of thousands of tourists who flock there during the summer when temperatures rise over 100° F. Another plant utilizing the vacuum-freezing process developed by the Israeli engineer Alexander Zarchin is also supplying converted sea water to the town's water system. This 250,000-gallons-per-day plant was developed by Desalination Plants, Ltd., a corporation jointly owned by Israel and an American firm.

The Negev Institute for Arid Research is doing intensive development work on electrodialysis systems, and has installed a 125,000-gallon-per-day plant at the T'seelim agricultural settlement in the Negev, where various membranes have been tested on well water containing 2,600 PPM of minerals.

In other research projects, the Israeli technical school, Haifa Technion, is studying the use of nuclear power for distillation of sea water under a contract with the International Atomic Energy Agency and recently announced it would begin building a pilot plant to test a new heat-transfer process, which could dramatically reduce the amount of tubing needed in large distillation units, and thus markedly reduce the cost of the desalted water. Other research is being carried on for the OSW at the Negev laboratory and the Weizmann Institute of Science. As Mr. Vilentchuk has said, "Israel cannot be satisfied with a 'static' state of the art of desalination, and is making efforts to contribute its share to the development of this new technology."

Mexico—Water-planning Microcosm

On May 8, 1967, Gordon Leitner, Executive Vice President of Aqua-Chem, Inc., one of the leading manufacturers of desalting plants, told the Tenth National Power Instrumentation Symposium of the National Instrument Society of America that the big desalting plant at Tijuana would make

Mexico a "leader in the application of advanced desalting technology."

Although Leitner's statement was based almost entirely on the construction of a single plant, which will be the biggest one on stream for only a relatively short time, his remarks reflect the fact that water planning has reached a high state in Mexico. The descendants of the great Aztec civilization, working with the United States and the International Atomic Energy Agency, are on the threshhold of what may become the greatest application of desalting technology ever undertaken—the construction of 1,000-MGD dual-purpose desalting plants.

These nuclear-powered plants, suggested by the joint U.S.-Mexican-IAEA study, have been described as technically feasible by Jack Hunter, head of the OSW. They are not on the drawing boards yet, but there is little reason to doubt that they will someday provide low-cost fresh water and electricity for the Mexican states of Baja California and Sonora, and for the arid regions of Arizona and California in the United States.

With the completion of the Tijuana plant, Mexico will have a major installation comparable in many respects to the Israeli plants at Eilat, but, like Israel, will look to a much greater water source in large-scale distillation units, yet to be built. Mexico also has small-scale experiments in agricultural communities, as does Israel. But the similarity to Israel begins and ends there. Israel needs desalting because it uses virtually all its water, while Mexico uses only 10 per cent of its water resources. Why is Mexico concerned with desalting technology when so much fresh water is theoretically available?

Manuel Anaya, an engineer and Secretary of the Hydraulic Resources Secretariat, attributes the need for desalting to the irregular distribution of other water sources. In many areas, development has increased the demand for water "to the point of exceeding the possibilities of supply for nearby sources . . . in those areas where topography, land, and climate do not combine in a balanced manner, backwardness and poverty are the consequence, in most cases because of water shortage."

Water-supply systems in Mexico date back many centuries to the early Aztec and other Indian civilizations. At least 382 irrigation works from the precolonial eras have been located. Additional water projects, including noteworthy aqueducts, which brought drinking water to the cities, were built during three centuries of colonial control ending in 1821. Some of these are still in use, 350 years after they were constructed. Additional waterworks, some outstanding in concept, were developed in the latter part of the nineteenth century and the early years of the twentieth century.

In 1910, Mexico began a period of armed revolutionary upheaval. The ensuing struggles changed its political structure and established a democratic system of government. The new political constitution of Mexico, proclaimed in 1917, says, "the land *and water* (italics added) within the boundaries of the national territory belong to the nation, which has had and has the right to transfer their control to private parties thereby constituting private property." Anaya says that the nationalization of water resources widened the scope of water use "to include complete exploitaton of this resource in order to achieve greater general benefits . . . eliminating the state and municipal barriers preventing distribution of water with greater equity in every part of the national territory."

As its first step, the Mexican Government in 1926 created the National Irrigation Commission, which, within its first twenty years, irrigated 420,000 hectares with new projects and 396,000 with substantially improved works. Included in this effort were many smaller projects operated by the users themselves, who organized into local water resources boards. In 1944, Mexico signed an international treaty with the United States that set forth the rights of both nations with regard to use of waters from the Colorado and Rio Grande rivers, both of which flow in both countries. The Rio Grande forms about 1,200 miles of the international boundary between the United States and Mexico. Recognizing that all uses of water, not just water for agricultural purposes, needed centralized direction and development, the Mexican Government late in 1946 created the Hydraulic Resources Secretariat, which further expanded the nation's water-resource development.

Between 1926, when the Mexican Government first became concerned with water planning, and 1966, the Mexican population grew from 15 to 44 million, the total area under cultivation increased 300 per cent, and the area under irrigation increased 400 per cent. Since 1946, when the Hydraulic Resources Secretariat was created to centralize water planning, population has almost doubled, increasing from 23 million to 44 million, and the number of people who have access to water has doubled, rising from 11 million to 24 million. This, however, still leaves 45 per cent of the Mexican people without a public source of water.

Of Mexico's total land area, most of which is mountainous, only 36 per cent is suitable for agricultural development, and of this, almost 65 per cent is arid, 30 per cent semi-arid, 5 per cent semihumid, and a very small percentage humid. All but the humid zones of this area would benefit from irrigation.

In estimating Mexico's water demand by the beginning of the 1980's, Anaya says the predicted population of 72 million will require about 103 billion cubic meters of water annually. Mexico will be able to supply 90 per cent of her population with water for home use and meet the agricultural and industrial needs, while using only 29 per cent of her total water resources. Mexico's water problem then, is not water shortage, but availability. It is the world problem in what might be termed microcosm. Much of the water is not where it is needed, and it will take extremely costly construction projects to bring it there, and available irrigation waters are becoming too saline to be usable. Improved drainage has been a partial solution, but it is quite likely that desalination technology will need to be applied to irrigation waters as the ground waters and river sources continue to salt up.

United Nations study teams found that many Mexican areas were having water problems, both quantitative and qualitative, and that these stemmed from the seasonal character of rainfall, insufficient recharge of underground sources, adulteration of fresh-water reserves by salts in the ground or excessive ground-water withdrawals. For such places as the islands of Cozumel and Carmen, the city of Mérida in Yucatan, the agricultural state of Sinaloa east of the Gulf of California, and the city of Guaymas in the state of Sonora (where a surface reservoir is dry most of the time) the U.S. experts felt that desalting would be needed in the near future.

The Colorado and Rio Grande rivers, providing water for the northern reaches of Mexico, are also growing increasingly saline. Under international treaty, the United States has taken steps to help solve this problem when the waters from these rivers become unusable in Mexico. But these steps have not permanently solved the problem, which is created by the drainage of human and saline-heavy agricultural waste water into the two rivers. With the growing pressure for more waters from these rivers to be diverted to Arizona, California, and other places within the United States, and the growing population along them, it is not likely that anything short of desalination, in both the United States and Mexico, can keep these waters usable when they reach Mexico.

One unusual Mexican water problem is that facing the capital, Mexico City, D.F. Parts of the city have sunk as much as thirty feet in the past thirty years as the result of large-scale pumping of water from underground sources beneath the city. Nearly 200 million gallons are taken daily from underground reservoirs in the soft clay beneath Mexico City. Mexico's Nuclear Energy Commission is considering an atomic-powered desalination plant which could take water previously unutilized from the nearby Lake Texcoco area, which is twice as salty as the sea.

The Mexican Government's water resources policy has eight points. Although desalination is only one of them, they offer a comprehensive checklist for water planning in developing nations:

1. Surveys and research on a national scale, for a better knowledge of streamflows and ground-water resources
2. Technical, academic, and practical on-the-job training for those concerned with plans for maximum water use
3. Practical instruction for the user, in order that water be used with maximum efficiency
4. Rational water distribution, in order that it be used where the highest economic and human benefit may be obtained from it
5. Financial aid to be repaid over long periods of time or in indirect form for areas of low economic levels
6. Water conduction at great distances and preferably at high levels
7. Encouragement of the regeneration and use of waste waters to avoid the pollution of streams and ground water
8. Desalination of sea water when development and its contingent food and industrial needs require it

The Puerto Penasco project, a Mexican experiment in controlled-environment agriculture involving a desalting plant, offers an unusual social value to developing countries by elevating the social status and living standards of the agricultural segment of the community.

The University of Arizona researchers working on the project recognize that, as in most developing nations, the field worker is at the lower end of the socio-economic scale and suggest that the objective of raising the level of the agricultural worker to that of his industrial counterpart is "one of the most important design considerations" in the creation of a new coastal desert community around a food-producing system. "For the controlled-environment system of agriculture this may prove to be relatively simple," they say. The worker in the greenhouse part of the system, specially trained for this new kind of agriculture just as the technician is trained for his role in the desalting plant, can have the same status and income as the other technicians in the community. The Arizona team reports:

> The greenhouse technician will have the same control over his project as does the factory worker. He will no longer be at the mercy of the often ungracious tricks of nature which previously lost him his crops. . . . Any effort to improve himself and his crops (under the new kind of agriculture involved) will be rewarded by increased benefit to himself and his family. The production of food can become one of the end products of the town's economy instead of simply the base as in the case of the peasant farm economy.

Desalting in Pakistan

In another part of the world, the role of desalting in a developing nation is perhaps best illustrated by one local situation. On the extremely dry Makran coast of West Pakistan is the fishing village of Gwadar, a community of 8,000 people near the Iranian border. If negotiations under way at this writing are successfully completed, Gwadar will be the site of the first solar desalting plant under the U.S. Agency for International Development's solar-development program. AID officials in Lahore have been negotiating with I. H. Usmani, Chairman of the Pakistan Atomic Energy Commission, who is responsible for finding water for the barren, sun-baked Makran coast, which stretches for 400 miles along the Arabian Sea, and covers terrain between Karachi and the Iranian border. Rainfall averages less than six inches annually. The drought is relieved only by rain that comes suddenly, in great amounts, but briefly, then leaves the desert just as it was, baking aridly in the sun. The scattered fishing villages exist in constant need of fresh water. Because the villages make a substantial contribution to Pakistan's foreign exchange from the sale of their catch, the government is anxious to provide them with a source of fresh water.

At present, Gwadar gets what fresh water it has from a natural cistern in the hills above the port, where rain water is preserved, and from brackish wells dug at the base of the sand dunes around the village. When rain does come, it percolates through the dunes to the rocky bottoms. Holes dug at the base of the dunes provide only a temporary source of water, sometimes only for a few hours. This water and the water from a handful of springs and wells in the area sells for $25 per 1,000 gallons, and in time of scarcity for $50. The fresh water required by the fish-freezing and -packing factory at Gwadar is trucked 300 miles from Karachi at a cost of $100 per 1,000 gallons.

The only alternative to a solar still is damming rivers inland from the port and piping the water to Gwadar. But in an area of persistent drought, the rivers are rarely adequate for this purpose, whereas the average of 3,330 hours of sunlight per year provides an ample supply of energy for the solar still. The projected still will provide only 25,000 gallons of fresh water daily, but it is predicted that it can double and perhaps treble the output of Gwadar's fisheries, which already earn $3 million annually in foreign exchange. And the water will cost only $2–$3 per 1,000 gallons.

Chairman Usmani, whose commission is already building nuclear power stations at Karachi and Roopur, is thinking also in terms of starting a dual-purpose nuclear desalting station at Sonmiani in the early 1970's. Sonmiani, a fishing port fifty miles from Karachi, is being developed to handle overflow commercial and industrial development from Karachi. By the next decade, Karachi will need considerably more electrical power than will be available from new facilities or those being built. Long-range action includes the possibility that a dual-purpose desalting plant at Sonmiani could also supply the additional power needed in larger Karachi, and that possibly a small conventional 500,000-gallons-per-day plant at Gwadar could provide the water and power that will be needed by Gwadar and other west-coast villages by that time.

In summary, this chapter has presented a view of the specific role desalting may play in the future of some of the world's developing countries. It has ranged from Kuwait, which gets all its water from desalting, to Israel and Saudi Arabia, which will be using desalination to augment existing natural sources, to Mexico, which has more water than it needs—but can't use it and hence must turn to desalination for help—to Pakistan. Every country has different problems, and the social and economic context within which the water problems must be solved ranges from ancient ways of doing things to highly sophisticated planning and development.

To cite one more particular country, not mentioned previously, and less significant at present than indicative of future directions, here is an item from the *Water Desalination Report* of July 20, 1967:

> Kenya's Minister for Natural Resources C. M. G. Argwings-kodhek held up desalting as something learned about in the U.S. which could bring great benefits to Kenya, upon his arrival there last week. The Minister said a desalting plant in Mombasa, the country's principal seaport on the East African coast, would eliminate that area's water deficits. Mombasa is now supplied by fresh water from the Mzima Springs. But a desalting plant for Mombasa would make the spring water available to solve water problems in the Tiata Hills area. A report on possible desalting equipment use in the Mombasa region, according to the Minister, will be ready within two months.

7

The Economics of Desalting

The Vice President of the United States stood on a platform in Key West, Florida, and talked about desalination. He was participating in the dedication of the new desalting plant built by the Florida Keys Aqueduct Commission. There were what are described as polite guffaws when Hubert H. Humphrey said that by 1980, nuclear-powered desalting plants would be producing a billion gallons of fresh water daily for 10 cents per 1,000 gallons.

Humphrey responded to the audible skepticism, ad-libbing a story about a group of men he was with in the 1930's who snickered at an aviation expert's prediction that jet planes would be flying at speeds of 600 miles per hour in the 1950's. Later in the day, he remarked that his estimate "will be one of the more conservative statements made here today."

While Vice President Humphrey talked in Key West, U.S. AID planners in Pakistan were negotiating for the construction of a smaller solar distillation unit—one-hundredth the size of the Key West unit—that would provide water costing $2–$3 per 1,000 gallons to substitute for water that now costs a fish-processing plant on the Makran coast 10 cents for just one gallon. Although still three to four times higher than the Key West price, in Pakistan that will be a bargain.

Actually, desalting is a bargain in both places. The Key West plant is producing water for 85 cents per 1,000 gallons from a plant that cost somewhat more than $3 million to build. The alternative was a $40 million aqueduct that would not be used to capacity for perhaps another thirty years, during which the people of Key West would have paid interest on a $40 million bond issue rather than on the much smaller one. Unfortunately, the economics of desalination are seldom so simple or obvious, for they are usually obscured in the general cloudiness of water economics. Experts say repeatedly that desalted water costs too much, but rarely do they know what conventional water supplies truly cost. It is frequently all but impossible in the United States and other developed countries to tell what the consumer is paying for his water. He may pay a water bill, plus taxes that cover a recreation development program that is involved in a regional water system, plus more taxes for a sewer system that includes wastewater treatment, and still more taxes for a watershed reforestation program carried on by a forestry agency, and still more taxes for street maintenance—which may well include the cost of tearing up streets to repair water mains. And, at the same time, his water bills are subsidizing cheap water for farmers who usually pay one-third to one-tenth what the home-owner is charged for water. It is quite possible that a man whose water bill reads 35 cents per 1,000 gallons may really be paying twice that much. Or, as in New York City, he may get no water bill at all, for his water charges may be hidden in overall real estate, sales, or income taxes.

In some countries, the cost of water may be three or ten times the amount paid by the average American water user, because water is scarce and it costs more to deliver it. Or it may be less—immediately, that is—because of government subsidies.

The point at issue when advocates of desalination talk to advocates of traditional waterworks such as high dams, 500-

mile-long aqueducts, or going down 800 feet or more to pump up ground water, is comparative cost. Many economists and water managers seem to see only comparative cents-per-1,000-gallons costs. They also tend to deal only with the needs of today and tomorrow; a committee preparing a book on cost factors related to desalination for the United Nations in 1962 looked only two or three years ahead, according to one of its members. This apparent short-sightedness, which focuses on immediate costs, overlooks the value of water. Other planners feel that value should be the prime factor in the social and economic equation used by a community or a nation in determining whether or not it wants to utilize desalination technology as all or part of its water plans for the future.

Discussing water costs in developing countries, U.N. expert Dr. Joseph Barnea, who has been quoted earlier in these pages, says:

> Where politically possible, the price at which water is provided should reflect the full cost, since the provision of water free of charge or at a very low price invites waste and lack of interest in bringing about improvement in efficiency of water use. Nor does it provide any economic incentive for investments in better irrigation systems, or in the re-circulation of water. In water-short countries such a policy thus becomes an obstacle to economic development.

Dr. Barnea touches an extremely sensitive public-policy nerve, but the issue is one that must be faced up to by all nations. In much of the world, the availability of water—or lack of it—has been taken for granted. Historically and traditionally, agricultural water has been subsidized—paid for by the home-owner and industrial operator through taxes and higher water rates. Developing countries seeking to increase their water resources—with desalination technology, through expensive mining and transport of underground water supplies, or by building high dams to create reservoirs—ultimately will have to find a way of paying for the water, either by government subsidy or by higher charges to the farmer.

There is, however, a growing awareness of the fact that cost, as such, may not be the prime factor in water economics. A *Washington Post* editorial dealing with the struggle over approval of a bill to give central Arizona more water from the Colorado River noted recently that, if federal funds were not appropriated, Arizona would probably raise the necessary funds to go it alone. "Officials in Phoenix are more worried about losing the water than about paying for the project."

The value of the water has become the prime consideration here—as it has in many, many places. Thus, Turkey, Finland, Spain, Pakistan, the United Arab Republic, Mexico, Greece, England, and many other countries are turning toward desalination because it holds promise of guaranteed water supplies available more quickly than they would be from other sources. Their decisions reflect value judgments based on the importance of having the water as soon as possible.

At a small, informal meeting during the International Conference on Water for Peace, a delegate from Italy, talking about the projected use of desalination in the arid southern regions of his nation, said, "Yes, we could get water from other sources, but it would take us twenty years. Why wait twenty years when we can get it in just three?" He was balancing the value of seventeen years with an adequate supply of water against the possibly lower cost of water that would be available twenty years hence.

And an Egyptian, talking about an experimental olive grove that utilized desalted water, was asked what the water cost. When he said 60 to 70 cents per 1,000 gallons, there were protests at the thought of paying that kind of money for irrigation water. He held his ground. "These are quality olives. It will be a high-income crop, a new industry for our people. We have our high dam for the people along the Nile River. Now we need water for the people on our coasts."

The word "cost" always causes confusion in any discussion

of the economics of desalination. It is relatively simple to put a dollars-per-1,000-gallons price tag on the "cost" of desalting hardware and its product, water. It is much more difficult to figure the "cost" to society of a village populated by children growing up half-fed amidst acres of untilled but arable land that is not farmed because there is no water to be spared for farming. Invariably, someone will ask if it would really "cost too much" to make that water available—or to provide a water supply dependable enough to prevent a factory from moving away to another location, or to assure the water necessary to end economic and social stagnation persisting where people, jobs, and food supplies depend on a supply that is either inadequate or almost nonexistent.

Vice Admiral Hyman G. Rickover not long ago said, "In my opinion the most damning thing you can say about cost-effectiveness studies is that they don't—and the types of studies they make render it impossible to—take account of human life. They do not believe that the good is as valuable as the profitable."

In the field of water supply, Admiral Rickover's condemnation of cost-effectiveness studies can be broadly applied. In the past, the potential benefits of water-engineering projects have been considered something to add onto the end of an engineering report without thorough examination. As recently as 1966, when Resources for the Future published a collection of papers presented at the seminars in water resources sponsored by that organization and the Western Resources Conference, water economists were being called to task for this approach.

Allen V. Kneese, the organization's director of Water Resources and Quality of Environment Programs, indicated in an introductory paper that recent work in the field is beginning to build a new basis for economic analysis of water systems by "emphasizing the external effects of water development and the impossibility of arriving at optimum development and use unless these are taken explicitly into account." Bringing the expertise of the engineer, the hydrologist, the economist, and the social scientist to bear on water problems is "perhaps the most important" development in the water-resources field in recent years, he said, adding, "the thought has now penetrated deeply that economic analysis is not something to be tacked onto a piece of engineering analysis after it is finished, in order to justify it." Economist Peter O. Steiner of the University of Wisconsin wrote that it is easier to determine the cost of a project than it is to determine the benefits it will supply, saying, "benefit measurement is hard and time-consuming, and should be undertaken only when required." Political scientist Hubert Marshall of Stanford added that "no real consensus has yet been reached on some aspects of the standards and criteria that are appropriate for the economic evaluation of water projects." Hence, "it is not surprising that bureaucratic norms take precedence over professional norms in the calculation of benefit-cost rations." And Harvard's Arthur Maass pointed to the fallacy of limiting benefit-cost analysis, as applied to public investment in the United States, to economic efficiency instead of potential social benefits, stating that such a limited approach may make benefit-cost analysis "largely irrelevant."

Water planning is a complex business, in which technology as such is applied to social needs. If the water planners can accept a broader role, and can incorporate into their planning processes the economist, the sociologist, the political scientist, and the agronomist, along with the engineering technologist, a great deal of traditional resistance to desalination will undoubtedly be overcome.

The planner needs to know the value of the water to the people, the city, the nation, the region for which he is making decisions. And he needs to understand the corollary benefits that stem from an improved water supply—the Keynesian "multiplier factor" of the benefits that accrue as the impact of a particular investment is felt. If an expensive piece of desalting hardware provides water that elevates living standards, enhances community development and industrialization, brings more food for a growing population, how expensive has it really been? And if the benefits can be attained in three years, instead of, perhaps, twenty, hasn't the hardware cost been amortized long before the payments are completed?

Water Costs per Thousand Gallons

The actual cost of desalted water has dropped steadily. In the early 1950's, the price tag on desalted water was about $5 per 1,000 gallons. Most of the plants operating today produce fresh water for considerably less than that, and the cost per 1,000 gallons keeps going down as technology improves, new energy sources are developed, and the desalination plants get bigger and bigger. The Key West plant produces fresh water for 85 cents per 1,000 gallons; the Tijuana plant will produce it for about 65 cents; the Israeli 100-MGD plant, it is estimated, will produce fresh water for 24–28 cents per 1,000 gallons, or perhaps for 8 or 9 cents less, if the new process developed by the Technion Institute proves feasible for large-scale use before the new plant is actually built; the even larger Metropolitan Water District of Southern California plant on Bolsa Chica Island, near Los Angeles, for 22 cents. Predictions are that even bigger plants, such as the projected billion-gallon facilities, will better than halve that last figure.

Dr. Jack Hunter of the Office of Saline Water says today that when one knows how much desalinated water will cost, one knows the maximum amount that should be paid for water in a given situation.

In 1965, Philip D. Bush, Vice President of the Kaiser Engineering Division of Kaiser Industries, told the U.S. Senate Subcommittee on Irrigation and Reclamation that "the reduction in the cost of desalted water will follow the same dramatic and inexorable path still being experienced in other and older basic industries." It was his prediction that the cost factor would be reduced by developments including better scale control, the ability to use greater heat levels in distillation units, the availability of lower-cost waste heat from nuclear, dual-purpose plants, new water-treatment methods, and the construction of larger modules with larger capacities. Bush also looked forward to the advent of less expensive hardware through the development of more efficient pumps, plastic-coated concrete components, and other innovations, and suggested further that now industrial and agricultural uses for desalted water would enhance its economic attractiveness.

Recent developments bear out these hopes. During the period in which this book was being written, new developments included a new reverse-osmosis filter, which offers promise of reduced costs; the manufacture of small desalting units made of lower-cost aluminum; a gas-turbine energy source, probably able to provide lower-cost energy for desalting plants; and the Technion method of heat transfer, announced late in November, 1967.

Progress in the development of breeder reactors, which will provide less expensive fuel for nuclear plants associated with desalting units producing only water, also gives promise of bringing down the cost of desalinated water, for the energy required to raise the temperature of salt water to the point where it turns to steam in a distillation plant is a major part of cost of operating such a plant. While nuclear energy does not desalt water by itself, its important contribution to desalination technology is that, for larger plants, it provides cheaper fuel. When the desalter is coupled to production of electricity, the economic advantage will generally be even greater, and there is the plus value inherent in the fact that nuclear power plants do not pollute the air as coal or oil burners do.

Factors Affecting Desalting Plant Costs

How does one determine how much a specific desalting plant will cost? If the plant is going to be large enough to make a substantial contribution, to a large water-supply system, its price will not be found in any catalogs. One excellent set of guidelines for determining the economic feasibility of desalting was prepared by J. R. Wilson of Kaiser Engineers and E. A. Cadwallader of the U.S. Agency for International Development. This relatively simple, step-by-step method for figuring the size of the required plant and the cost of the water it will produce is being used by AID in its desalination-funding program. (It is reprinted in this book as an appendix, pages 193–214.) Other useful documents to assist water planners in such determinations include the U.N. publication *Water Desalination: Proposals for a Costing Procedure and Related Technical and Economic Considerations* and the International Atomic Energy Agency's Technical Reports, Series No. 69, *Costing Methods for Nuclear Desalination.* The U.N. publication is probably the most thorough in its exploration of the many factors involved, especially in developing countries.

Among the factors that these publications consider important over and beyond the actual cost of plant fabrication are:

Location. This may be affected by the single- or dual-purpose nature of the plant, whether or not the plant uses nuclear energy or existing energy sources, in which case the plant would have to be located in reasonable proximity to the power supply. Land costs and the cost of transporting water from the plant to the distribution system are other location factors involved.

Energy sources. Although nuclear energy may be cheaper,

it may be economically and socially more desirable to utilize locally available heat sources or fuels such as oil, coal, waste gas from oil plants, waste heat from existing electric plants, factories, incinerators, and the like. If locally produced coal or oil is used, this, again, is a plus in terms of stimulation of the local economy.

Quality of water to be desalted. The saltier and more mineral the water—or the more foreign matter in it, as would occur around a seaport—the higher the cost of desalting will be. It may be desirable to locate the plant away from the worst area, on an estuary or at a distance from a port or oil-loading facility. This decision would raise the cost of water conveyance even as it lowers the process cost.

Financing. The construction of a desalting plant involves both large capital investments and continual expenditures for operating the plant, amortization of the investment, insurance, replacement parts, and the ultimate replacement of the plant over a twenty- or thirty-year period, depending upon the way it is figured. Interest rates alone can be a major factor in the ultimate cost of the product water.

Available labor. Whether the plant can be built and operated by local labor, with local supervision, directly affects the cost of the plant, its operation, and the product water. In many instances, the plant will have to be constructed and put into operation by the manufacturer with imported labor; in others, this may be shared, with even some part fabrication undertaken by the purchasing country or area. Now, simple pipe for conveying the water can be produced locally under licensing by the manufacturer. If local people can operate and maintain the plant, new jobs are added to the local economy. However, the question of automating the operation as opposed to using relatively unskilled local labor arises. The drawback of automation is the question of the availability of parts and of someone to replace broken or malfunctioning equipment. The use of automation does not make for major savings in labor costs and can cause extensive periods of nonproduction if maintenance is a problem because of lack of personnel.

Foreign exchange. The relative amounts of foreign and local currency needed during construction and operation of a plant will be affected by the kind of plant selected. If, for example, there is a considerable variation in daily water needs it may be found expedient to build a smaller plant— using foreign-exchange currency—and a larger storage unit paid for out of local currency.

The Larger Considerations

All of these are specific considerations in determining the costs of a desalting plant, per se. But what about the larger economics of desalting itself? Part of the answer comes from the economics of improved water supplies. What do you get for your investment, in addition to the water itself?

Improved health, for one. Waterborne illness still remains at the top of the world's public-health problems. Waterborne diarrheal disease alone in 1964 was estimated to have caused 5 million deaths throughout the world. In Japan, the installation of safe water supplies in thirty rural areas reduced communicable intestinal diseases by 71.5 per cent, trachoma by 64 per cent, and the death rate of infants and young children went down 51.7 per cent.

Some economists maintain that improving health conditions depresses the economy because it increases the population and the demands for food and goods. But such an effect is usually short term. People whose health is good do not remain burdens on the economy. They become boosters. It is the chronically ill who are burdens. Reports from members of the World Health Organization show water shortages as one of the principal factors for continuing low social and economic levels in their countries, and in 1959, the World

Health Assembly said, "safe and adequate supplies of water
. . . are indispensable for economic and social development."
Studies made in Latin America show a direct relationship between life expectancy at birth and per-capita earning capacity.
Good water means more national health, productivity, and
income.

More water also means more food. In Mexico, for example,
spectacular success in raising wheat yields is due not only to
improved crop varieties but also to the shifting of much of the
wheat acreage onto irrigated land. In many countries, salty irrigation drainage can be re-used through desalting processes
or by being conserved and used for crops that are more salt
tolerant, thereby greatly increasing total food production.

But, beyond these basics, what else must be considered?

Two University of California engineering professors, J. M.
English and N. El-Ramly, addressed the Second European
Symposium on Fresh Water from the Sea in Athens in May,
1967. Their paper was an excellent analysis of the short-
sighted application of traditional cost-accountant water economics to decisions involving the use of desalination. By and
large, desalting installations have been limited to areas of
"highly valued demand" that are easy to define and require
relatively little water, areas where desalting is the only alternative or has very obvious economic advantages (as along
Pakistan's Makran coast, or in Bermuda), or where the required plant capacity and related investment are relatively
small in comparison with other alternatives. In these situations, they said, there is little room for argument over
whether the investment is justified. Another point they made
is that when some or all of the above conditions do not exist,
economic evaluations are usually based on the cost of water
produced by a single plant. This is the cost which is compared
with other choices.

"We contend that this approach may result in uneconom-
ical decisions," the Californians contended. "It may well be

that a higher unit cost for water from a desalination plant as compared with other sources is justified. The economy of desalination should be considered from the point of view of the total system of which it may be only a component."

Another "serious shortcoming of conventional evaluations" they identified is the tendency to view desalting plants as having a twenty-year life when comparing them with other water resources. This, they said, may be as much because some economists feel it is difficult to extrapolate costs beyond two decades as because they feel the plant will need replacing within that time. Some experts figure thirty years. Others include the cost of replacement as part of the annual operating cost by including annual contributions to a sinking fund for such purposes. In any event, where planning ahead more than twenty years is concerned, population growth can be projected with reasonable certainty, along with indicated changes in living standards. Such long-range forecasts are important, even when short-term investment is considered, for the long-range water needs ultimately determine the total characteristics of a water-supply system.

In their report, English and El-Ramly also emphasized that many alternatives to desalting may be limited themselves, both as to total quantity and increasing salinity, and that in the long run desalination may eventually be required. Thus, an initial investment in desalination to provide water to augment or blend with conventional sources may be the best answer to the long-range solution of a specific water problem.

There is also the question of who can afford the water. Water-pricing policies are so widely varied that William Bowen, writing in *Fortune* magazine, described them as "pervaded with irrationalities and contradictions." Such contradictions are especially vivid in California—where a multimillion-dollar water project is bringing water from the northern to the southern part of the state, while the Metropolitan Water District of Los Angeles sells water below cost, making up the difference through a special property tax—and in Tucson, Arizona—where water comes from the deepening of wells at great cost, while Tucson residents pay less for water than they would in Indianapolis, St. Petersburg, or other communities in the East where water is not so hard to obtain.

"Subsidizing water is a pleasant custom, but it belongs to a time of water abundance," the *Fortune* writer maintained. Costlier methods of supplying or treating water, caused by shortages or pollution, are steadily boosting the price of conventional water supplies, so that subsidies must either rise—to keep the cost to the consumer down—or be decreased in the hope that higher costs will limit consumption.

Another water expert, Luna B. Leopold, who heads the U.S. Geological Survey's Water Resources Division, says forthrightly that "we have always obtained water for bargain prices. We must steel ourselves to a new conception of what water really is worth. And," he adds, "one other thing seems certain—rising water costs are making desalination increasingly competitive with traditional water sources."

In Saudi Arabia, the ability of municipal and industrial water users in Jedda to pay for desalted water is accepted as a fact of life. Insofar as irrigation is concerned, that nation sees the basic problem as one of improving the use of water by the farmer, so that he can improve his income. His Excellency, H. E. Mishari, Minister of Agriculture and Water, says of the farmer, "the greater his income and margin of profit the more leeway he has to pay a higher price for his water, and the greater is the value of the water development to the nation as a whole." His view is that water that supports subsistence farming only is of very low value, whereas water used to farm high-value crops with an assured market at good prices has "almost unlimited value" to a country.

This view is in contrast to that held by some water planners in India who reject desalting because 31 cents worth of desalinated water will only earn 25 cents for a rice farmer using old-fashioned farming methods. This approach overlooks the fact that a guaranteed, dependable water system might produce two or three rice crops annually and that the yields of such crops, when new fertilizers and methods are applied, might raise the income of the farmer well beyond the 31-cents-per-1,000-gallons price of the water he uses.

An Israel writer, B. B. Jessel, in an article in *Israel Youth Horizon,* adds another economic factor to the discussion, saying the cost of desalting should be compared not with existing sources but with alternative new water sources. What's more, says Jessel, "water is too much of a necessity in life to be treated solely in economic terms . . . it is socially desirable that water should be just as readily available to the poor as to the rich . . . farming cannot be judged purely by economic criteria, but must be seen also as a way of life which is of social and cultural value to the nation as a whole." Again and again, the issue comes back to the social values of water in general and desalinated water in particular.

Another factor that must be included in the economic equation within which desalting projects are viewed is time. Where conventional waterworks are planned, the time lag from plans to construction and completion frequently exceeds twenty to thirty years. More time is lost in the political steps that must be taken even before construction begins— the agreements that must be achieved with various political subdivisions when a new reservoir will flood an area or water is to be diverted from one place to another or a pipeline must cross international boundaries. Negotiation of the Columbia River agreement between the United States and Canada took twenty years. The planners responsible for the imaginative North American Power and Water Alliance, which could bring water from the far north to many parts of the United States and Mexico, estimate thirty years for completion of construction—exclusive of the political time factor, which could well extend the duration to fifty years or more. Plants with a

1,000-MGD capacity could be supplying much of the same areas with potable water far sooner. Desalting plant construction is a short-term project. Amortization of costs takes time, but while the construction cost is being paid, the water is available and being used.

The people of southern Italy, Tijuana, the Netherlands, and many other areas will be enjoying the economic benefits of desalination within the next two or three years, whereas they might have waited two or three times that long for those benefits from other sources, if such sources could be found.

Desalination offers still other economic advantages. The plants can be built in modules, increased in size as needed, and geared to the expansion of power plants and electricity needs, or they can be constructed separately, and apart from such considerations. Plants can be built and financed in conjunction with power production and the availability of mineral by-products from the water processing. The technology can be made to fit a wide variety of socio-economic situations, whereas high dams, big reservoirs, and ground-water pumping are more limited in terms of flexibility, especially where there is a need for short-range water-supply expansion.

Funds for water-resource development come from a variety of sources. The World Bank (more properly called the International Bank for Reconstruction and Development) puts about half of its investments into such projects. The Inter-American Development Bank, too, is financing many major water and irrigation projects. U.N. agencies, U.S. AID, and a number of individual countries do some funding. And, of course, many countries use their own funds. Some projects are financed by a combination of government, industry, and private citizens, with the degree of participation dependent upon the degree of benefit. In still other projects, federal governments share the costs with localities and private utilities.

Ultimately, the user pays, through taxes and water charges,

unless he is highly subsidized—and then other users are paying part of his share. There are many who feel that increasing water charges will result in better use and less waste, by industries, home-owners, and farmers. But, in a number of places, the user may have to be taught how to save water or utilize it properly. User education is especially important in relation to the use of desalted water in agriculture. Intensive re-education of farmers to the use of nonwasteful irrigation methods, new irrigation cycles, and fertilizers can sharply increase the crop yield per thousand gallons of water used. New farming methods can make maximum use of relatively costly water.

Any country in need of more food, and preparing to invest in desalting to get water to augment its arable land, must include an all-out farmer-education program in its planning package. Such training may mean changing a traditional way of life, but it may also mean the survival of future generations who cannot be fed by old-fashioned food-growing methods.

Mohamed Shoaib, Vice President of the International Bank for Reconstruction and Development, said, at the International Conference on Water for Peace:

> In any large enterprise, of course, a certain misallocation of resources is unavoidable. But the excuse of ignorance and lack of understanding is no longer quite as valid as it might have been in earlier times, when waste was a camp follower of progress. The structure of industrial society in Europe and North America has taken seven generations to build. For the better part of 200 years, the principal guide was trial and error. The process involved much dissipation of human life and of irreplaceable resources. In the wake of phenomenal gains, it threw up unhappy consequences which are all too familiar. A few of these, such as water shortages and pollution, might have been avoided if what we know today had been known 50 or 100 years ago.
>
> Instead, much of our current knowledge has accumulated in the last few decades. . . . Today we have a vast and strikingly

new store of knowledge and experience which gives us the capability of greatly reducing the time and easing the task of development burden on our generation.

This new store of knowledge and experience places a heavy burden on water planners, for they must tread the still uncertain path between the traditionalists of old-fashioned water economics and the promulgators of new approaches to water-supply problems—including the advocates of desalination—and at a moment in history when time appears to be running out on them and on the world.

8

Now and in the Future

The world-wide need for water planning and water management takes into account the building of new dams, diversion of existing surface waters from one place to another, discovery and use of additional underground water supplies, re-use of waste waters and recycling of waters in industry, the possibilities of weather modification, and desalination. But it seems evident that desalination will be shouldering more and more of the burden of providing usable water.

Admittedly, many water planners still view desalination as a relatively minor contributor to total water supply. However, recent technological advances in the desalting field have reached the stage where large-scale application is both feasible and desirable, and at the same time, realistic evaluations of traditional water sources are beginning to show that desalting is becoming economically competitive. In the vital context of human needs, which are growing so rapidly that in some places there is almost no time left in which to prepare to meet them, the use of desalination technology has become socially desirable, if not imperative.

In recent months, nuclear-powered, dual-purpose desalting and electric plants have been proposed as a solution to Middle East tensions. There has been a knowledgeable prediction that 1,000 American cities must turn to desalination within the next ten years because their existing sources of supply may otherwise become unusable. In one particular situation, special legislation has been introduced because a new reservoir, built at a cost of several million dollars, can be used only if a desalination plant is built to treat the water it holds, or if an entirely new source of water is found.

OSW Progress

Despite advances and needs, however, the technology of desalting still has a long way to go before it lives up to its ultimate promise, and some critics remain ready to write it off. When the Office of Saline Water's appropriation last came up for renewal in the U.S. Congress, Representative John P. Saylor of Pennsylvania, an inveterate opponent of OSW expenditures, objected to additional appropriations on the grounds that the promise of low-cost fresh water from desalination, made when the OSW was created in 1952, had not been realized after fifteen years. He was ready to abandon the government's relatively small investment in desalination, ignoring the fact that the OSW has made remarkable progress in one generation.

The Office of Saline Water was created by the Eighty-second Congress in Public Law 448, "An Act to provide for research into and development of practical means for the economical production, from sea and other saline waters, of water suitable for agricultural, industrial, municipal, and other beneficial consumptive uses, and for other purposes."

The first paragraph of this 1952 Saline Water Act explained the reasons for the legislation:

> . . . in view of the acute shortage of water in the arid areas of the Nation and elsewhere and the excessive use of underground waters throughout the Nation, it is the policy of the Congress to provide for the development of practicable low-

cost means of producing from sea water, or from other saline
waters, water of a quality suitable for agriculture, industrial,
municipal and other beneficial consumptive uses on a scale
sufficient to determine the feasibility of such production and
distribution on a large scale basis, for the purpose of conserv-
ing and increasing the water resources of the nation.

The initial appropriation, to cover a five-year period, was
$2 million.

In 1955, the act was revised and extended to run through
1963, with a total authorization of $10 million. The new
legislation modified the research provisions of the law and
included participation of the Atomic Energy Commission and
the Civil Defense Administration. In 1958, the Congress
passed a joint resolution further expanding the OSW role in
the desalting field.

The language of the resolution pointed up the problems
already facing the nation at that time:

> . . . the United States population is multiplying at a rate
> which by 1980 will triple the demand for supplies of fresh
> water, which if not available will adversely affect the national
> defense by jeopardizing the economic welfare and general well-
> being of vast segments of the population of the United States,
> as well as the population of some of our territorial possessions,
> . . . many cities, towns and rural areas are already confronted
> by shortages of potable water that imperil health . . . the ex-
> panding population, industry and agriculture of the United
> States are becoming increasingly dependent upon assured aug-
> mented supply of fresh water while the future welfare and na-
> tional defense of the United States rest upon increased sources
> of fresh water.
>   . . . research by governmental agencies, educational insti-
> tutions, and private industry, has brought about the evolution,
> on a limited scale, of methods of desalting sea water and the
> treatment of brackish water which give promise of ultimate
> economical results . . . the United States Government has the
> responsibility, along with safeguarding the national defense,
> and protecting the health, welfare, and economic stability of
> the country, to transfer these experiments into production tests

on a scale not possible of achievement otherwise . . . it is in the national interest to demonstrate, with the least possible delay, in actual production tests the several optimum aspects of the construction, operation and maintenance of sea water conversion and brackish water treatment plants.

This resolution authorized the construction of five plants, each to utilize a different process. Another $10 million was provided and was used to build the demonstration plants at San Diego (the one ultimately moved to Guantanamo); Wrightsville Beach, North Carolina; Freeport, Texas; Roswell, New Mexico; and Webster, South Dakota. The original act was extended again in 1961 and in 1965, with appropriations to run through 1967 and, later, through 1972.

Through the end of fiscal 1966, the OSW had spent a total of $81,458,000 on all of its activities. The budget for fiscal 1967 was $27,500,000 for research and development and $2,351,000 for additional activities. It was hoped that a comparable sum would finally be made available for fiscal 1968. (The Atomic Energy Commission also has funds included in its appropriation for research and development for desalination purposes.)

All told, this does not represent a tremendous investment. By space-age scientific standards, to have spent $81,458,000 on technical research and development over a period extending from 1952 to 1966 is penurious. The total is less than the proposed investment by the federal government in the supersonic transport plane, less than is spent on a single moon shot, less than the annual budget for most of the individual national institutes of health.

The Second Annual Report on Saline Water Conversion, issued by Secretary of the Interior Douglas McKay in 1954, indicates that overcoming scientific disinterest in the field was a big problem faced by the infant program. Reporting that only about $300,000 of the $400,000 budget had been spent, obligated, or even tentatively committed in the first five months of the fiscal year, Secretary McKay reported:

> As with any research into the unexplored, the chances of attaining the objectives of the program depend upon the extent to which genuine scientific interest can be enlisted. . . . Although some scientists and engineers were at first hesitant to participate in the program, excellent cooperation by these groups now prevails and most of the known leaders in the field have offered their assistance.

The 1954 report listed only eleven research contracts, and the illustrations and text look like a collection of miniature working models and Model-T Fords compared to today's reports, projections, and working models.

The 1966 report listed hundreds of research contracts with universities, industry, foreign countries, and other federal agencies, as well as extensive developmental activity at the five demonstration site locations, one of which—Wrightsville Beach—is the world's leading desalination research center. There was no air of apology whatsoever in Secretary of the Interior Stewart L. Udall's covering letter transmitting the report to President Johnson. He wrote:

> One measure of progress in the endeavor to develop low-cost desalting processes is the application of the technology that has been developed to provide an incremental source of fresh water. People around the world soon will be using an additional 22.5 million gallons daily of fresh water produced from saline sources as a result of contracts awarded to U.S. manufacturers of desalting equipment during 1966. A survey of major desalting equipment firms in this country reveals they were awarded contracts or received letters of intent for the construction of some two dozen desalting plants. These plants are under construction, or soon will be, in the United States, the Caribbean, Middle East, Africa, South America and the Pacific. In addition, U.S. firms are in contention for contracts to construct plants in other locations as a result of bids opened during the

year, but for which contracts have not yet been awarded. . . .
Distillation and electrodialysis are the desalting processes being
utilized in these plants, with much of the technology becoming
available through research and development work sponsored
by the Office of Saline Water.

Whereas Secretary McKay had apologized for not being
able to spend $400,000, Secretary Udall was projecting budg-
ets rising to $43 million by 1970.

Subsequently, in 1967, Congress authorized the construction
of test beds, which are larger versions of demonstration plants
and fill a void between the pilot plant and the large prototype. Congress also authorized federal financial participation
in the development of the Metropolitan Water District plant
in California through both OSW and Atomic Energy Commission contributions to the construction of the desalting
units and the nuclear reactor. In this project, Secretary Udall
said, the federal government, private and public utilities, and
a public water agency are working as a team to "demonstrate
the reliability and maturity of dual-purpose technology under
actual operating conditions." The project also offers an opportunity to gain experience and to expedite "the development of large-scale desalting plants on an accelerated construction schedule."

In the area of engineering development, emphasis has been
on providing what Secretary Udall called the "best possible
processes at the earliest possible date." Distillation processes
still "command a virtual monopoly today for sea-water conversion . . . and are expected to continue to maintain a
dominant position during the coming decade," but the OSW
has been moving ahead with development of the reverse-
osmosis method, which originated in its research program.
Reverse osmosis, the Secretary said, has "progressed from a
laboratory curiosity to the point where it is now beginning to
be sold for specialty water production." The process is potentially usable not only for desalting brackish waters and, even-

tually, sea water, but is usable also in work on such problems as irrigation return flows where the salinity is high, demineralizing acid mine waters, and treatment of sewage. Industrial applications are being explored. Some may use reverse osmosis to recover valuable chemicals, others to concentrate fruit juices and beverages, others to remove water from crude oil, and still others to produce special waters for industrial use.

During the year, the OSW continued also to work on the development of electrodialysis, especially for use with inland brackish waters, and on advancing the potential of the freezing processes. Its researchers were exploring some of the basic problems of water composition and behavior, in the hope that they might come up with still undiscovered processes for desalting water at even lower costs than are now projected.

Quietly Spectacular Development

In 1953, an obscure scientist at the AEC's Oak Ridge National laboratory wrote a paper on the potential of atomic energy as a fuel for large-scale desalting plants that would provide low-cost water for agriculture. Although the paper made sense at the time, many thought he was indulging in the speculative fantasy of science fiction. Fourteen years later, the same scientist, Dr. R. Philip Hammond, presented his dynamic plan for food factories, in which nuclear-powered desalting plants would transform coastal deserts into world food resources costing pennies per day for each person fed—and those who heard him at the International Conference on Water for Peace had every reason to take him seriously.

At Wrightsville Beach, more than a dozen different prototype plants have been tested and new antiscale and freezing processes explored. The British, the Italians, the Dutch, the French, the Israelis, the Russians, the Japanese, the Germans, and others are involved in extensive process research and development. There are two desalting newsletters published in the United States, one in Europe, and a desalting magazine in Israel. The University of Glasgow offers a post graduate course in desalting technology, the University of California and McGill University have special courses, and many other universities do research in the technology or its applications. Meanwhile, more and more sizable desalting plants are going on stream and providing fresh water or fresher water where it did not exist in adequate quantities before.

The dedication of the Key West plant last year overshadowed the later dedication of the Clair Engle experimental plant in San Diego, but both have an important place in determining the future of desalting. The Key West plant proved the technical and economic feasibility of desalting for a small-sized community. Even though the Key West plant may have only a thirty-year lifetime (unless replacement of parts as they wear out extends it), it proved a highly acceptable alternative to an aqueduct costing more than ten times as much. The San Diego plant will not only produce 1 MGD of water, but will also be a major testing ground for components designed for the Bolsa Chica Island plant farther north on the California coast. And that plant will prove out the components and processes for plants two to ten times as large.

The step-by-step evolutionary development of big desalting plants has been quietly spectacular. Manufacturers such as Westinghouse and Weir Weisgarth say they are ready to build 50- to 150-MGD plants tomorrow, if someone wants to buy them. The Russians, too, are building a big plant, which will produce 100 MGD or more. And it may well be that the Israelis will decide to invest in a plant of such size without waiting for OSW's proving out—simply because time will not permit them to.

It is unlikely that there will be dramatic new breakthroughs in the desalination field comparable to those in medicine or aviation or space technology. Experts in the field are inclined to the view of slow but persistent progress described by Phillip D. Bush of Kaiser Engineers in his 1965 testimony to a Senate committee. There will be improvements in the efficiency of distillation processes as larger and larger plants are built, and there will be improvements in the longevity and capability of membranes used in other processes, such as reverse osmosis and electrodialysis.

Presently, the OSW projects the longevity of distillation plants on a twenty- to thirty-year basis, but this is predicated to a large extent on the assumption that improvements will mean today's plant may be outmoded by the late 1980's. Within ten years, it is predicted, reverse osmosis will be applicable to sea water on a large-scale basis, and this development will affect the plants to be built after that happens. (It will also, of course, affect the cost of the product water.)

None of this means that the world's water planners and water users will be sitting around waiting to see what happens. Some planners—especially those who are acutely conscious of cost per 1,000 gallons—may prefer to watch and wait, while continuing with hydrological surveys and searches for underground aquifers. But the need for fresh water grows daily, and new industrial processes continue to expand the need for higher-quality water supplies.

That the OSW spends, comparatively, so little money may tend to demean the importance of desalination technology in the public mind. The technology is not so complicated that huge sums need be devoted to continuing research. The construction of a 150-MGD plant may involve thousands of miles of tubing and thousands of valves, large pumps, scale-prevention processes, and the like, but it is not nearly as complex as the intricacies of the life-support system and telemetry in a single space capsule, tiny by comparison to a nuclear-powered desalting plant.

Here is one of the anomalies of desalination technology and its recent progress. One can write about a desalting plant capable of producing enough fresh water from the sea to meet the water needs of a city of 750,000 people and speculate about the future when plants ten times that size will be built along the Gulf of California and elsewhere, but somehow water supply does not excite the public imagination. It is a subject generally taken for granted, except in panicky moments of temporary drought-born shortage, or times when, as in Arizona, it becomes a political issue, or, as in Israel and Saudi Arabia, an inescapable matter of national necessity.

At Wrightsville Beach, there is nothing amazing to behold. The handful of scientists and engineers there use words like "pad," just as their fellows do at Cape Kennedy down the coast. But the collection of boilers, tanks, pumps, and pastel-shaded tubing that covers part of the twenty-five acres is static. There are no countdowns, no rockets rising from great clouds of smoke and flame. When the Key West desalting plant went on stream, there were no newspaper photographs of fresh water to compete with photos radioed back from the moon.

Yet, to social scientists or government planners worrying about how to feed twice as many people a generation hence, the most thrilling sight in the world may well be a field of vegetables growing where before there was barren land, or a woman turning on the tap in a kitchen to get water for cooking.

Desalting's spectacular values are in the improved living standards of the beneficiaries—better food on their tables, new houses, new jobs.

National Observer reporter Walter A. Damtoft wrote after visiting Aruba's new desalting plant:

Aruba is hardly industry-poor as Caribbean Islands go. It has been the site of one of the world's largest oil refineries since 1929. . . . But automation has come to Lago; an employment roster that once exceeded 8,000 is down to 2,000 and still dropping, new industry is being sought to take up the slack. The effort has been modestly successful; thin wisps of yellowish smoke mark new chemical and fertilizer plants. . . . It is, to be sure, understandable that Arubans—and Key Westers—delight in no longer having to drink brackish water or water drawn from rain-water cisterns, in which it is necessary to keep small fish to eat mosquito larvae. But it is the yellowish wisp of smoke and the luxury hotel abuilding in Aruba and the plans for new motels and homes in Key West that are the significant testimonials to a new here-and-now technology— water desalination.

Damtoft's "here-and-now technology" is available at this moment for application to water-supply problems in many parts of the world. It may not be as efficient as it will be in the future, but it is available, and it is being used on an ever increasing scale.

During 1967, in the Spanish Sahara, negotiations were going on between the Spanish Government and several industrial firms interested in the development of large phosphate deposits. A 1-MGD desalting plant will be required to provide water to process and wash the phosphate pebbles and separate them from their natural matrix. The water will be piped inland about sixty miles from the desalting plant at El Aiun on the coast. But where will the end result be visible? Not at El Aiun. Not at the phosphate mines. Change will come miles away in Spain, where the phosphate fertilizers will be used to improve local agriculture.

Today, in Oklahoma, the visible evidence of desalting's value may be seen in advance of its probable use at the new Foss Reservoir. The $7.5 million reservoir and aqueduct system, designed to store waters from the Washita River for 40,000 residents of the area, was completed in 1965. But the river water—like the water in so many rivers today—proved unfit for human consumption. Although initial estimates were that it would contain 750 PPM of dissolved solids— above U.S. Public Health Service minimum standards but still used in many places—the Washita River now has a level of 1,780 PPM of totally dissolved solids, three and a half times the acceptable minimum. Because the original estimate of the river's contamination level came from a federal agency, there is a bill in Congress to provide federal funds for a 3-MGD desalting plant, costing $2 million, to make the river waters in the reservoir fit for municipal and industrial use. Today's technology was not available when this particular reservoir was planned. But it is interesting to note that the cost of a desalting plant to process Washita River water is only slightly more than one-fourth the cost of building the dams, aqueducts, and other parts of the reservoir system it will "rescue."

One of the misunderstandings many people have about desalination arises from centuries of emphasis on the creation of fresh water from the sea. It is quite likely that the immediate expansion of the technology will involve not the desalting of sea water but widespread application to inland waters that have become too mineralized or saline for use, or underground waters that are not potable or pure enough for either agricultural or industrial purposes.

Inland water-supply contamination has created international water-quality problems along the Rhine, the Colorado, and the Rio Grande. It has led to broad desalination technology plans in the Netherlands, Finland, and Israel, to name just three places. Such contamination will become more and more of a problem as irrigated, populated, and industrialized areas expand.

President Fred A. Loebel of Aqua-Chem, Inc., who, as a child in Milwaukee, Wisconsin, watched his parents boil water to make it drinkable, and whose firm has built or is building many of the largest desalination plants around the world, talked to the American Public Works Congress in Boston in October, 1967. Pointing to the future of desalination for purification of inland brackish water, he said:

> While conventional water treatment methods still can be utilized in many areas of the country, the rising levels of pollution—to which we see no end in sight as yet—plus the rising

demands of a growing population and industry for more and better water, will require the use of newer methods which rid water of a higher proportion of its contaminants than ever before. In the race for industrial development, convention business, tourism and population service, a growing number of communities will, in the next few years, be reviewing their entire approach to the water problem.

As the situation looks today, as many as 1,000 towns and cities throughout the U.S. may be forced to convert their brackish or saline water for drinking and other purposes within the next ten years.

Dr. D. B. Brice of the International Atomic Energy Agency indirectly forecast another rapidly growing use of desalination technology at the 1967 Istanbul Symposium on the Use of Isotope and Radiation Techniques in Soil Physics and Irrigation Studies. He said that, if single-purpose desalting plants powered by breeder reactors were used to produce irrigation water for just one-tenth of the world's needs for new food supplies during the next thirty years, their growth rate would equal or exceed the growth rate of electric power reactors.

It is obvious that, in many parts of the world, desalting will be linked with nuclear power development. In many instances, nuclear energy will provide an energy source less expensive than those now available. At least half of all new electric-power-generation plants being built in the United States and Great Britain today are nuclear powered. There will be parallels between the improvements in nuclear and desalting technologies. Probably the most significant aspect of this relationship is the evolution of breeder reactors, which manufacture their own fuel, for single-purpose plants producing only water. Hitherto, the high cost of nuclear-power installations was such that the capital investment made economic sense only if the plants would generate large amounts of salable electricity in addition to producing water. The advent of smaller breeder receptors capable of supplying lower-cost energy in areas where oil, coal, or gas is not readily available will, undoubtedly, have a profound effect on the future use of desalination as a source of fresh water.

At the Istanbul Symposium, Professor Mel A. Hagood of the Food and Agricultural Organization laid stress on the fact that water not fully used is becoming scarcer and scarcer and costly to develop and deliver. Thus, he said, there is growing competition for the future use of water, in general, and for water traditionally used for agriculture, in particular. He also said there are no universally accepted criteria for determining how much agriculture can pay for irrigation water; the justifiable cost depends on a country's need for water and soil resources for food, for international trade, and for its over-all economy.

Water To Cool the Middle East

Perhaps the most outright acknowledgment of desalination's potential is the suggestion—made by Lewis L. Strauss, former chairman of the Atomic Energy Commission, and sponsored by former President Dwight D. Eisenhower—that the United States build massive dual-purpose desalting plants in the Middle East in an effort to bring peace to that part of the world. In essence, this plan, which has been endorsed by Republicans and Democrats alike in the U.S. Senate, and was considered by that body in the autumn of 1967, says that the need for water and power for economic development contributes to the antagonisms and conflicts in the Middle East. The construction of several dual-purpose plants, providing all the water that might be needed and a tremendous amount of electric power for industrial and other development besides, would eliminate major causes of friction and lead the Arabs and Israelis into peaceful codevelopment of the whole region.

Although nobody challenges the suggestion that more

water and more electricity would solve many Middle East problems, it must be remembered that Eric Johnston's plan for peaceful use of the Jordan River waters foundered not long ago on the inability of Arabs and Israelis to work together. And some partisans of the Strauss proposal failed to recognize that U.S. participation in comparable activities in the Middle East had been going on for some time. Testifying on this point before the Senate Foreign Relations Committee in mid-October, 1967, Secretary Udall said, "The U.S. Government has cooperated closely with Middle Eastern states in applying developing technology to the area's water problems."

Such cooperation has included the joint U.S.–Israeli study of the feasibility of a 100-MGD plant proposed for Ashdod; OSW work with Saudi Arabia on the design of a fossil-fueled, dual-purpose desalting and power plant for Jedda; discussions with Kuwait on possible cooperation in research related to some aspects of desalting and the training of operations personnel; and the negotiation of an understanding with Iran for the joint study of water resources and requirements on which to develop a plan for meeting Iran's water needs.

The Strauss proposal sufficiently recognized that the area has a long way to go before it can absorb the amounts of electric power envisioned and that, with the exception of Israel, no nation in the Middle East is in a position to absorb the large additional amounts of water involved. It is something akin to building grand new six-lane highways in a developing country that has few automobiles.

Secretary Udall offered, instead, a step-by-step concept of what could be done in the way of developing water and other natural resources in the Middle East: "The solution of the Jordan River water problem and the displaced persons crisis lends itself to a comprehensive regional solution," he said. "The first step would be the development of the Jordan River to meet its maximum capability. Attention should then be directed to supplementing the naturally available Jordan River water supply in other ways."

He noted that the combined development plans of Israel, Jordan, and Syria would require almost 500,000 acre-feet of water more than would be available from the Jordan River, the main water resource in the area. Some additional water— perhaps one-fifth of that needed—could be provided by cloud-seeding over the Jordan to produce additional rainfall, but it would depend on the amount of moisture in the atmosphere at the proper time and the consent of all the nations on which the rain might fall or from which it might be diverted.

Ground-water potentials are nearly fully developed in Israel, Secretary Udall said. Some ground water is available in eastern Jordon. Water re-use and conservation would provide additional water resources.

But it was to desalination that he turned for the largest part of the answer to the area's historic water problems. One great advantage desalination technology offers is that it does not take water away from one area and give it to another. Thus, it eliminates the political and social struggles that so often arise around water-diversion projects, as they arose to negate the Johnston plan for use of the Jordan River.

In testimony that proved to be a review of desalination past and a prediction of desalination to come, Secretary Udall commented that, at the time Congress approved the Saline Water Bill, in 1952, "desalted water had been used only as a method of obtaining fresh water for ships at sea and in a few isolated arid areas of the world. I can think of no other commodity that would do more to quench the fires and tension that exist in the Middle East than an abundant supply of fresh water. . . . The technology to supply that water is within our grasp."

His testimony continued:

Since its inception, the entire thrust of the Department's desalting program has been to develop lower and lower cost methods of producing fresh water from saline sources. While remarkable progress has been achieved, there are still some who contend that this water is still not cheap enough to use for irrigation. But the use of desalted water for irrigation in the Middle East cannot actually be compared to existing irrigation projects anywhere else in the world. . . . If a few hundred million dollars investment in a desalting plant could in any way contribute to the prevention of a future conflict, it may indeed be the wisest investment of our time.

We do not advocate that a plant be built to raise agricultural products which are readily available in other areas; but provided with the life-giving water, I am convinced that the fertile lands of the Middle East could produce high-value cash crops to meet the rising demand for food and fiber throughout the world. . . . Planning could begin today. . . . The same design that is being developed for the Bolsa Island project could be utilized. . . . Technology available today in desalting makes it possible to consider a wide variety of plant sizes and processes to meet the supplemental water requirements existing in the Middle East. . . . Desalting plants can be built in capacities to meet conceivable short-term and long-term water requirements of the population, providing for the needs of the thousands of refugees and displaced persons. . . . In areas where abundant low-cost fossil fuel is available, desalting plants can be constructed within a period of less than two years at reasonable water costs.

Within Our Grasp

Secretary Udall's key point was "the technology to supply that water is within our grasp." He could have been talking about Mexico, Pakistan, the southwestern United States, South Africa, or the Soviet Union. And he was talking about right now or, at least, the immediate future.

In a way, he echoed the intensity of the participants in the small "sidebar" session at the International Conference on Water for Peace, who crammed themselves into a small meeting room to seek answers to their individual national water problems. He echoed the meaning of the Egyptian who didn't think 60 cents per 1,000 gallons of water too high a cost to irrigate a quality olive crop, the Italian who thought twenty years too long to wait for what water desalination could bring in three, the Englishman who advocated using desalting plants to keep reservoirs at optimum levels during periods of drought or maximum use, the American who talked of the multiplier factor that produced so many social and economic benefits from the installation of desalination plants, and the Israeli who discussed blending desalted water with other water to grow oranges.

Secretary Udall's testimony projected the general application of desalting technology—whether by a floating desalination plant moving from coastal village to coastal village or by a 1,000-MGD facility sucking up vast quantities of ocean and turning out water of almost pristine purity—that has as its end result something so simple as filling a glass from a kitchen tap or watering a tomato plant.

Simple, but life-giving.

Guidelines for Determining Feasibility of Desalination

Presented at the International Conference on Water for Peace by J. R. Wilson, Kaiser Engineers, and E. A. Cadwallader, Agency for International Development.

Many countries are experiencing a rapidly growing demand for additional freshwater sources to accommodate the anticipated growth of industry, agriculture and population. As an area's water requirements increase, the development of available freshwater sources becomes increasingly difficult and expensive. If nearby natural sources of fresh water have already been utilized to near their ultimate capacity, it is imperative that economical alternate sources be found—otherwise a nation's development may be stifled.

Advances in desalination technology have reduced the cost of desalting seawater and brackish water to such an extent that, in certain areas, it is competitive with the cost of water obtainable from new natural water supplies. Thus, desalination has added a new dimension to water supply planning, and should be given consideration as a means of supplying future water needs in many water-short areas.

Determination of the economic feasibility of desalination, however, should be undertaken as part of an overall plan to define and resolve the water shortage problem. This paper provides guidelines for developing this overall plan and, since approximate capital cost of seawater desalination facilities and unit cost of water produced therein are required in developing the plan, provides a method of approximating these costs.

The solution to the water shortage problems of a country or region should be sought in a series of logical steps, progressing from the point where a present or future water shortage is recognized to the point where a commitment is made for a specific facility. Development of this overall plan usually requires the establishment of an administrative agency such as a water development board, and a technical agency such as a study organization. Figure 1 illustrates the steps such agencies would require in developing the plan.

In seeking the solution to the water shortage problems, consideration should be given first to the development of present freshwater resources and then to the production of potable water by desalination of seawater or brackish water.

In the logical sequence of steps leading to the solution of the water shortage problems, the following documents should be produced:

(1) The Water Development Plan—which provides a definition of the water shortage problems and summarizes all of the possible alternative solutions.

(2) The Preliminary Feasibility Studies—conducted to evaluate the various alternative solutions and identify the most promising solution(s) for further study, and

(3) The Detailed Engineering Feasibility and Economic Study —the results of which would serve as the basis for a commitment for the design and construction of a specific natural water or desalination facility and as a basis for

the preparation of an Economic and Technical Soundness Analysis.

The Water Development Plan

The first step in the search for the solution to the water shortage problems of a country or region is the assembly and evaluation of background information on the water and energy resources of the area. A study organization should carry out and evaluate a number of concurrent surveys to obtain this information as well as information on possible solutions to the problems; it should then summarize all the information in a document called the Water Development Plan.

Evaluations of energy requirements and resources should be an integral part of the Water Development Plan since the solution of water shortage problems is, in general, related to the production or use of energy.

The suggested sequence for the surveys, definitions and evaluations which culminate in the formulation of the Water Development Plan is shown in Figure 2.

After the background surveys are completed, at least in preliminary form, steps may be taken to define the overall water shortage problems and to set forth possible solutions.

To determine possible *Natural Freshwater* solutions to the water shortage problems, the development of the freshwater sources inventoried in the preceding surveys should be defined and reviewed. This review comprises a concise compilation of resources and a determination and preliminary evaluation of possible solutions.

To determine possible *Desalination* solutions to the water shortage problems, a review should be made of the utilization of desalination processes for obtaining fresh water from the sources of seawater or brackish water identified in the preceding surveys. This review should consider and evaluate

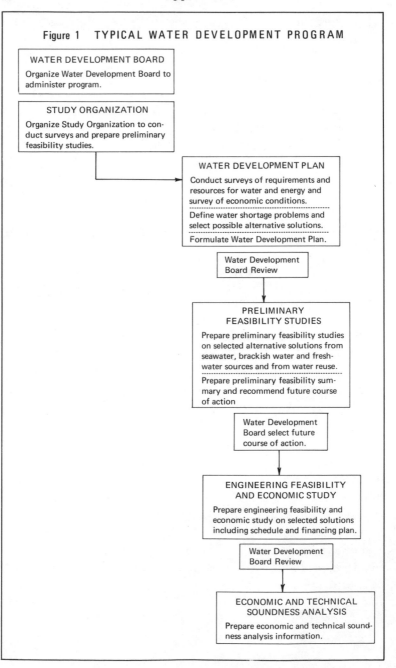

Figure 1   TYPICAL WATER DEVELOPMENT PROGRAM

WATER DEVELOPMENT BOARD
Organize Water Development Board to administer program.

STUDY ORGANIZATION
Organize Study Organization to conduct surveys and prepare preliminary feasibility studies.

WATER DEVELOPMENT PLAN
Conduct surveys of requirements and resources for water and energy and survey of economic conditions.
Define water shortage problems and select possible alternative solutions.
Formulate Water Development Plan.

Water Development Board Review

PRELIMINARY FEASIBILITY STUDIES
Prepare preliminary feasibility studies on selected alternative solutions from seawater, brackish water and freshwater sources and from water reuse.
Prepare preliminary feasibility summary and recommend future course of action

Water Development Board select future course of action.

ENGINEERING FEASIBILITY AND ECONOMIC STUDY
Prepare engineering feasibility and economic study on selected solutions including schedule and financing plan.

Water Development Board Review

ECONOMIC AND TECHNICAL SOUNDNESS ANALYSIS
Prepare economic and technical soundness analysis information.

the characteristics of the brackish and seawater sources, and make a preliminary evaluation of possible desalination solutions.

Since definitive cost estimates will not be possible at this point for either the natural freshwater or desalination solutions, approximate rough estimates should be made of each alternative as a guide in determining possible solutions requiring further study.

Capital costs of possible natural freshwater solutions can be made by engineers experienced in similar construction projects. Because of the limited experience in construction of desalination facilities, however, it may be more difficult to secure rough estimates for desalination. In such cases the following procedure and accompanying notes and nomographs (found at the end of the paper) may be utilized to determine approximate capital costs and unit costs of water for seawater desalination facilities under conditions which will be used in the preliminary feasibility studies. Estimating aids for brackish water desalination facilities have not been included, as the variation in costs due to local water conditions requires a more detailed approach. Since seawater desalination processes may be utilized on brackish water sources, the seawater desalination costs may be used as the upper limit of the costs of brackish water desalination.

Desalination Facility Capital Costs

The first step in preparing the capital cost approximations is to establish the following preliminary design conditions (Notes 1 and 2 at the end of the paper may be useful in establishing these values):

1. Plant capacity in gallons per day (gpd)—see Note 1.
2. Plant operating factor—see Note 1.
3. Economy ratio—see Note 2.

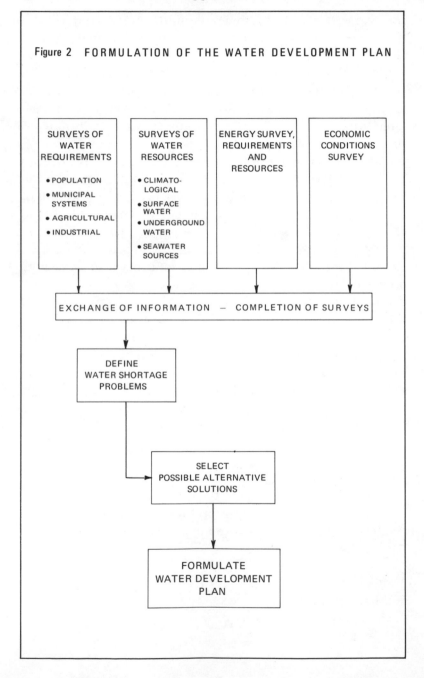

Figure 2   FORMULATION OF THE WATER DEVELOPMENT PLAN

Having selected the nominal plant capacity, the plant operating factor and several economy ratios (in accordance with the preliminary feasibility study requirements and the corresponding notes), one may begin the determination of the estimated desalination facility capital cost. This is accomplished in the following manner:

1. Determine the unit desalination plan capital cost for each cconomy ratio by utilizing the Unit Desalination Plant Capital Cost Nomograph, Figure 4.
2. Determine the desalination plant capital cost for each economy ratio by multiplying the unit desalination plant capital cost determined above by the nominal plant capacity. Tabulate the results in Table I below.
3. Determine and tabulate the heat source capital cost for each economy ratio, as described in Note 3.
4. Determine and tabulate the product water conveyance capital cost, as described in Note 4.
5. Determine and tabulate the land capital cost, as described in Note 5.
6. Determine and tabulate the other capital costs and contingency, as described in Note 6.
7. Complete Table I and determine the unit facility capital cost by dividing the total desalination facility capital cost by the nominal plant capacity.
For examples, see Table III.

TABLE I
DESALINATION FACILITY CAPITAL COST

Economy ratio

Desalination plant capital cost	——	——	——	——
Heat source capital cost	——	——	——	——
Product water conveyance capital cost	——	——	——	——

Land capital cost — — — —
  Subtotal — — — —
Other capital costs and contingency — — — —
  Total Desalination Facility
    Capital Cost — — — —
Unit facility capital cost, $ per daily
  gallon — — — —

Unit Cost of Water

Before utilizing the nomographs and notes (at the end of the paper) to estimate the unit cost of water, it is necessary to establish the following preliminary feasibility study conditions:

1. Fixed charge rate—see Note 7.
2. Unit cost of fuel—see Note 8.
3. Hourly labor cost—see Note 9.
4. Chemicals and other costs—see Note 10.

Having determined the fixed charge rate, the unit cost of fuel and the hourly labor cost, the estimating of the unit cost of water may be accomplished in the following manner:

1. Determine, and tabulate below, the fixed cost component (for each economy ratio) by utilizing the Fixed Cost Component Nomograph, Figure 5.
2. Determine, and tabulate below, the fuel cost component (for each economy ratio) by utilizing the Fuel Cost Component Nomograph, Figure 6.
3. Determine, and tabulate below, the labor cost component by utilizing the Labor Cost Component Nomograph, Figure 7.
4. Determine, and tabulate below, the chemical and other unit costs, as described in Note 10.
5. Total the above to determine the unit cost of water. The economy ratio that results in the lowest unit cost of water will then be evident.

TABLE II
UNIT COST OF WATER

Economy ratio

Fixed cost component	——	——	——	——
Fuel cost component	——	——	——	——
Labor cost component	——	——	——	——
Chemical and other unit costs	══	══	══	══
Total Unit Cost of Water	——	——	——	——

Note: The above approximations used in determining the unit cost of water treat the nondepreciable items of land and working capital as though they were depreciable items, whereas a lower fixed charge rate (excluding depreciation and insurance) should be used on these items. This error, however, is small in relation to the other uncertainties of this estimate.

Preliminary Feasibility Studies

By utilizing the rough cost estimates of alternative water problem solutions, the alternatives that should be included in the feasibility studies can be identified. The first step in the implementation of a water development plan is the performance of preliminary feasibility studies on the possible solutions. This will furnish a water development board with the information necessary to select the most appropriate and advantageous course of action. The consideration of each alternative solution should include the preliminary feasibility studies, evaluations and cost estimates necessary to determine the capital costs, annual costs and unit cost of the water. These studies should be made on facilities that would provide the desired production or capability in accordance with the Water Development Plan timetable.

In the examination of alternative solutions, design capacity is an important consideration. Either desalination or the development of underground freshwater resources would follow the water development timetable in numerous but small steps; a large hydrological basin development would, however, provide a large amount of water at once (Figure 3). Such considerations play an important role in the determination of the plant operating factor (the ratio of the amount of water that a facility actually produces during a year to the amount of water that the facility would produce during the year if it were operated continuously at its design output), which in turn, affects the unit cost of water.

Figure 3

METHODS OF MEETING THE DEMAND CURVE

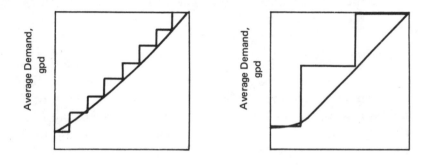

(a)   (b)

Since the preliminary feasibility studies will be used both for comparing alternative solutions and as the foundation for more detailed studies on the selected alternative(s), they should be performed on an equitable basis. This will sometimes require determination of the capital cost and unit cost of water on a present worth basis.

Completion of the feasibility studies, as shown in Figure 1, will provide a water development board with the data necessary to select the future course of action that promises the most suitable solution(s) to the water shortage problems.

Engineering and economic feasibility studies can then be conducted on the selected solutions, and action taken to implement the plan for solving the water problems.

Notes and Nomographs

Most of the seawater desalination plants built or proposed in the past several years have utilized the multistage flash evaporation process and were designed for a top brine temperature of 200F to 250F. Other leading seawater desalination processes, however, have capital and operating costs generally comparable to those of the multistage flash plants. Therefore, while the Unit Desalination Plant Capital Cost Nomograph is based on multistage flash evaporator plants, it may be utilized for other leading seawater desalination cost approximations.

Note 1—Nominal Plant Capacity and Plant Operating Factor

The nominal plan capacity is usually expressed in gallons per day—the amount of product water that will be produced when the plant is running at design conditions. Every desalination plant, however, must be shut down occasionally for preventive maintenance and for repair of tube leaks and other unscheduled outages. The water that a plant can be expected to produce each year is not 365 times its design daily capacity, but is some factor (less than 1) multiplied by 365 times its design daily capacity. This factor is the plant operating factor, which is defined as the ratio of actual annual water production to the quantity of water that could be produced annually if the plant were operated continuously at full rated output. The plant operating factor usually is expressed as a percentage value. A plant operating factor of

90% has been assumed to be achievable in some feasibility studies for single-purpose plants.

Therefore, the nominal plant capacity should be selected to secure the required annual product water production with a reasonable plant operating factor (usually 90% for single-purpose plants or 80% to 85% for dual-purpose electric-power water-desalination plants).

The Unit Desalination Plant Capital Cost Nomograph is based on desalination plants consisting of only one module (module capacity and nominal capacity are the same). When plants of several modules are being considered, the unit desalination plant capital cost and the desalination plant capital cost should be determined for each module (by using module capacity for nominal capacity). The sum of the capital costs of the modules should be used as the desalination plant capital cost in Table I.

Note 2—Economy Ratio

Seawater distillation plants require saturated steam at approximately 25 psig. (Low cost steam to as low a pressure as 10 psig may be utilized with only a small increase in desalination plant capital cost.) One measure of plant performance is the economy ratio—defined as the pounds of product water produced per pound of steam supplied to the plant. The appropriate economy ratio to use in the plant design must be determined by optimizing the design for lowest unit water cost. For low unit cost of fuel and relatively high fixed charge rates, a low economy ratio (4 to 6) may be optimum. For high fuel costs and low fixed charges, a higher economy ratio may be optimum.

The nomographs may be used as a means of approximating the optimum economy ratio by selecting a value (usually about 8) and performing the necessary calculations to determine the unit cost of water. Then, values of economy ratio higher and lower than 8, say 6 and 10, should be selected and the new unit cost of water determined for each. These calculations should be continued until an economy ratio is found that results in the lowest unit cost of water.

Note 3—Heat Source Capital Cost

The approximate capital cost of an oil or gas fired boiler may be determined by the following empirical equation:

$$\text{Heat source capital cost} = 0.55* \text{ x } \frac{\text{nominal plant capacity (gpd)}}{\text{economy ratio}}$$

*An empirical value determined by boiler cost-capacity correlations.

Note 4—Product Water Conveyance Capital Cost

To determine the approximate capital cost of the product water conveyance, determine the miles of conveyance required and multiply by the typical cost per mile, from the table below.

Nominal Plant Capacity, gpd	Pipe Diameter, Inch	Typical Cost/Mile
100,000	4	$ 6,500
200,000	6	18,000
300,000	8	22,000
500,000	8	22,000
1,000,000	10	27,000
2,000,000	12	32,000
3,000,000	16	43,000
4,000,000	20	57,000
5,000,000	20	57,000
7,500,000	24	71,000
10,000,000	24	71,000

Note 5—Land Cost

The desalination plant capital cost estimates determined by use of the nomograph include typical cost of on-site improvements such as surveys, roadways and paved areas but excludes land cost.

The land required to accommodate a desalination facility of 1 million gpd capacity is approximately 2 acres. For a desalination plant facility of 10 million gpd approximately 10 acres are required. In addition to the cost of the land itself, the land cost should include allowance for site access and such costs as surveys, right of ways, access roadways, and unusual site development work. Since these capital costs vary greatly with location and site conditions, estimates should be prepared by those familiar with the proposed site and with local site development costs.

Note 6—Other Capital Costs and Contingency

Other costs required to construct and operate a desalination facility are:

a. The cost of engineering, design, inspection and procurement
b. The owner's expenses prior to commercial operation of the facility including start-up
c. Interest during construction
d. Working capital including allowances for inventory costs of fuel, chemicals, materials, and supplies; for insurance prepayment; for spare parts inventory and for accounts receivable.

While the nomograph used in estimating the desalination plant capital cost is based on actual plants and estimates of proposed plants, which may in some cases include contingency, it is appropriate to include a contingency in this cost estimate as well.

To provide an allowance for other costs and contingency, a percentage of the cost of the desalination facility may be used. A value of 20% of the cost estimate of the desalination facility (sum of desalination plant capital cost, heat source capital cost, product water conveyance capital cost and land capital cost) is recommended as the allowance for other capital costs and contingency.

Note 7—Fixed Charge Rate

Whenever possible, the fixed charge rate on capital investment should be based on factual information for the specific project. For study evaluations and projects on which the actual fixed charge rate is not available, a fixed charge rate may be developed by the method outlined below.

The fixed charge rate on depreciable capital comprises the following elements:

a. Interest charges
b. Depreciation
c. Interim replacements
d. Property insurance
e. Federal income taxes (none in the case of a municipal utility)
f. State and local taxes

In the case of a utility operated by a government entity, the interest charges would be representative of the interest rate at which bonds could be sold by that government agency. Once the interest rate and plant life is known, the depreciation can be determined from depreciation tables. For depreciable capital, the sum of the interest rate plus depreciation is the amortization rate that will recover the capital investment over the depreciation period. Note that in the case of nondepreciable capital, such as land and working capital, no depreciation or interim replacement is applied and insurance is applied only to inventory items such as spare parts.

For a detailed engineering study of a proposed desalination plant, the allowance for interim replacements of tubes and other plant components may be based on a detailed projection of tube failure rates (for a distillation plant) as a function of plant life. Lacking such a detailed analysis, a value of 1% may be added to the fixed charge rate to allow for interim replacement. This value is approximately correct for a 15-year tube life and a 30-year plant life. It should be noted that interim replacements are sometimes included as an operating cost element, rather than as a component of fixed charges for the approximate cost estimates outlined herein.

Annual property insurance may be taken as 0.2% of the depreciable capital cost—this is a typical average value for utilities such as fossil-fueled power plants.

A municipally-owned utility does not pay federal income taxes but may incur state and local taxes, or costs in lieu of local taxes.

Tabulated below is a typical breakdown of fixed charge rates for a municipally-owned utility, assuming 4% interest rate and a 30-year plant life.

	Depreciable Capital, %	Nondepreciable Capital, %
Interest charges	4.0	4.0
Depreciation (30-year sinking fund basis)	1.8	—
Interim replacements	1.0	—
Insurance, property	0.2	—
State and local taxes (or costs in lieu of local taxes)	1.4	1.4
Total Fixed Charge Rate	8.4%	5.4%

Note 8—Unit Cost of Fuel

The unit cost of fuel (oil or gas) is the cost (in cents per million Btu—higher heating value) at the plant site. The unit cost should include transportation and unloading costs and demand charges.

Note 9—Hourly Labor Cost

The hourly labor cost is the wages paid each hour to the plant staff plus allowance for overhead and for general and administrative expenses. Because the day shift may include an operator and several maintenance men, whereas the night shifts may have only operators, the wages should be determined by dividing the weekly or monthly total wages (including overhead and general and administrative expense) by the total hours in the same period.

Note 10—Chemicals and Other Unit Costs

The chemicals required for a seawater desalination facility include H_2SO_4, chlorine and caustic. The other unit costs include electric power for pumps, instruments and lighting. An allowance of $0.08 per 1,000 gallons should be made for the chemical and other unit costs.

TABLE III
EXAMPLES OF DESALINATION FACILITY CAPITAL COSTS AND UNIT COST OF WATER

	EXAMPLE 1			EXAMPLE 2			EXAMPLE 3			
Nominal plant capacity, gpd (see Note 1)	1,000,000			250,000			10,000,000			
Plant operating factor (see Note 1)	90%			95%			90%			
Economy ratio, lb product/lb steam (see Note 2)	8	10	12	6	8	10	8	10	12	14
Fixed charge rate (see Note 7)	8%			12%			7%			
Fuel cost, cents/million Btu (see Note 8)	25			35			30			
Hourly labor cost (see Note 9)	$14			$9			$20			
Conveyance, miles	4			2			6			
Plot size and land cost	3 acres @ $6,000 per acre			1 acre @ $2,000 per acre			10 acres @ $5,000 per acre			
Desalination Facility Capital Cost, dollars										
Desalination plant capital cost (see nomographs)	1,000,000	1,250,000	1,550,000	342,000	425,000	525,000	4,000,000	4,900,000	6,050,000	8,000,000
Heat source capital cost (see Note 3)	69,000	55,000	46,000	23,000	17,000	14,000	690,000	550,000	460,000	390,000
Product water conveyance capital cost (see Note 4)	108,000	108,000	108,000	44,000	44,000	44,000	430,000	430,000	430,000	430,000
Land capital cost (see Note 5)	18,000	18,000	18,000	2,000	2,000	2,000	50,000	50,000	50,000	50,000
Subtotal	1,195,000	1,431,000	1,722,000	411,000	488,000	585,000	5,170,000	5,930,000	6,990,000	8,870,000
Other capital costs and contingency (see Note 6)	239,000	286,000	344,000	82,000	98,000	117,000	1,030,000	1,190,000	1,400,000	1,770,000
Total Desalination Facility Capital Cost	1,434,000	1,717,000	2,066,000	493,000	586,000	702,000	6,200,000	7,120,000	8,390,000	10,640,000
Unit facility capital cost, $/daily gallon	1.43	1.72	2.07	1.97	2.34	2.81	.62	.71	.84	1.06
Unit Cost of Water, cents/1,000 gallons										
Fixed cost component (see nomograph)	35	41	51	68	83	99	14	15	18	23
Fuel cost component (see nomograph)	31	24	20	57	43	34	37	30	24	21
Labor cost component (see nomograph)	38	38	38	99	99	99	6	6	6	6
Chemicals and other unit costs (see Note 10)	8	8	8	8	8	8	8	8	8	8
Total Unit Cost of Water	112	111	117	232	233	240	65	59	56	58

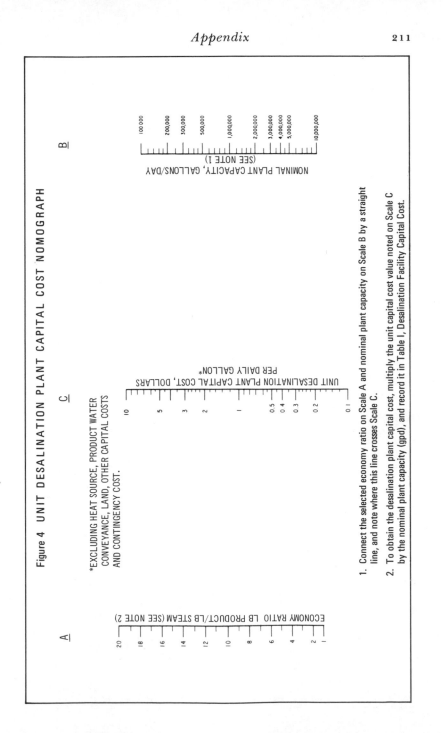

Figure 4 UNIT DESALINATION PLANT CAPITAL COST NOMOGRAPH

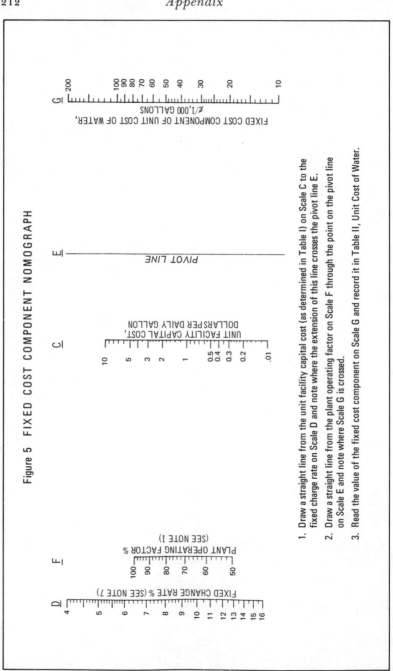

Figure 5 FIXED COST COMPONENT NOMOGRAPH

G FIXED COST COMPONENT OF UNIT COST OF WATER, ¢/1,000 GALLONS

C UNIT FACILITY CAPITAL COST, DOLLARS PER DAILY GALLON

E PIVOT LINE

F PLANT OPERATING FACTOR % (SEE NOTE 1)

D FIXED CHANGE RATE % (SEE NOTE 7)

1. Draw a straight line from the unit facility capital cost (as determined in Table I) on Scale C to the fixed charge rate on Scale D and note where the extension of this line crosses the pivot line E.

2. Draw a straight line from the plant operating factor on Scale F through the point on the pivot line on Scale E and note where Scale G is crossed.

3. Read the value of the fixed cost component on Scale G and record it in Table II, Unit Cost of Water.

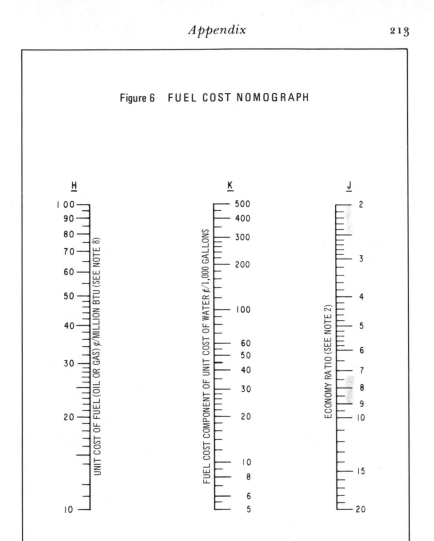

Figure 6 FUEL COST NOMOGRAPH

1. Draw a straight line from the unit cost of fuel on Scale H to the economy ratio on Scale J, and note the crossing of Scale K—fuel cost component of unit cost of water.

2. Read the value on Scale K, and record it in Table II, Unit Cost of Water.

Appendix

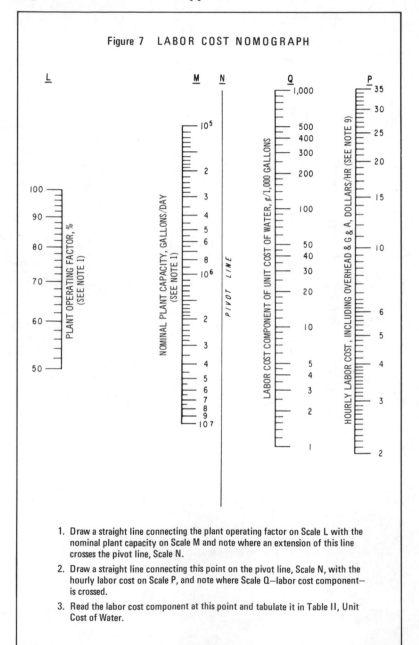

Figure 7   LABOR COST NOMOGRAPH

1. Draw a straight line connecting the plant operating factor on Scale L with the nominal plant capacity on Scale M and note where an extension of this line crosses the pivot line, Scale N.

2. Draw a straight line connecting this point on the pivot line, Scale N, with the hourly labor cost on Scale P, and note where Scale Q—labor cost component—is crossed.

3. Read the labor cost component at this point and tabulate it in Table II, Unit Cost of Water.

Bibliography

ADLER, NANCY. "Desalting Plant's Link to Whales Provokes Dispute," *The New York Times,* January 8, 1967.

American Water Works Association. *Better Water for Americans.* New York, 1967.

Aqua-Chem, Inc. *Annual Report.* Milwaukee, Wisconsin, 1967.

Aqua-Sol, Inc. *Fresh Water from the Sea.* Minneapolis, Minnesota, 1967.

ARAD, N.; MULFORD, S. F.; and WILSON, J. R. *Multistage Flash Evaporator Plant Operating Factor.* Kaiser Engineers, Oakland, California (no date).

Armour Corporation. Baldwin-Lima-Hamilton Division. *Annual Report.* Chicago, 1967.

Associated Press. "Key West Turning to Sea for Water," *The New York Times,* July 9, 1967.

BATISSE, MICHEL. "The International Hydrological Decade." *UNESCO Courier,* Paris, July, 1964.

Bechtel Corporation. *Saline Water Conversion.* San Francisco, California, 1966.

BOWEN, WILLIAM. "Water Shortage Is a Frame of Mind," *Fortune,* April, 1965.

BOYKO, HUGO. "Salt Water Agriculture," *Scientific American,* March, 1967.

BRADLEY, CHARLES C. "Human Water Needs and Water Use in America," *Science,* October 26, 1962.

BRADY, THOMAS F. "Saudi Arabians Raze a Palace To Build a Desalting Plant," *The New York Times,* February 15, 1967.

British Information Services. *Desalination and Its Role in Water Supply.* London, 1967.

BURLEY, M. J. and MAWER, P. A. *Desalination as a Supplement to Conventional Water Supply.* Water Research Association, Medmenham, England, April, 1966.

BUSH, P. D.; FINKE, J.; and WILSON, R. J. *Variables in the Design of Large Dual-Purpose Plants.* Kaiser Engineers, Oakland, California, 1967.

BYLIN, JAMES E. "Water Worries," *The Wall Street Journal,* April 12, 1965.

CARR, DONALD E. *Death of the Sweet Waters.* New York: W. W. Norton, 1966.

Central Institute for Scientific, Technical and Economic Information. *Water Economy.* Warsaw, Poland, 1966.

COWEN, ROBERT C. "Water Seekers Inch Forward," *The Christian Science Monitor,* January 26, 1965.

CRAIGHEAD, F. C., JR., and CRAIGHEAD, J. J. *How To Survive on Land and Sea.* U.S. Naval Academy, Annapolis, Maryland, 1943.

DAMTOFT, WALTER A. "In Caribbean Ports, New Flow of Fresh Water," *The National Observer,* September 18, 1967.

DENTON, D. A. "Evolutionary Aspects of the Emergence of Aldosterone Secretion and Salt Appetite," *Physiological Reviews,* Melbourne, Australia, April, 1965.

"Desalting: ET & E World Survey," *Environmental Technology and Economics,* Stamford, Connecticut, May 25, 1967.

DEWEY, DOUGLAS R. "Germination of Crested Wheatgrass in Salinized Soil," *Agronomy Journal,* Vol. 54, 1962.

DUKERT, JOSEPH M. "Desalting Makes Economic Sense," *Manage,* National Management Association, Dayton, Ohio, May, 1967.

DURANTE, RAYMOND. "Future Programming in Office of Saline Water," in *Water Production Using Nuclear Energy* (R. G. POST and R. L. SEALE, eds.) Tucson: University of Arizona Press, 1966.

FENTON, RONALD S. "Where We Stand with Water Desalting," *UNESCO Courier,* Paris, July, 1964.

FORMAN, JOHNATHAN, and FINK, OLLIE. *Water and Man: A Study in Ecology.* Columbus, Ohio: Friends of the Land, 1950.

FURR, J. R.; CARPENTER, J. B.; and HEWITT, A. A. *Breeding New Varieties of Citrus Fruits and Rootstocks for the Southwest.* Address before Rio Grande Valley Horticultural Society, Weslaco, Texas, January 22, 1963.

FURR, J. R.; REAM, C. L.; and BALLARD, A. L. *Growth of Young Date Palms in Relation to Soil Salinity and Chloride Content of the Pinnae.* Report 43, Date Growers Institute, 1966.

GILLON, PHILLIP. "Drinking the Sea," *The Jerusalem Post,* March 11, 1966.

Government of Kanagawa Prefecture. *Water Utilization in Kanagawa Prefecture.* Yokohama, Japan, May, 1967.

Government of Japan. Ministries of Health and Welfare, International Trade and Industry, Agriculture and Forestry, and Construction. *Planning and Economics.*

"Greek Isle Begins To Desalt Water," *The New York Times,* October 12, 1964.

GYUL, K. "The Caspian Sea Will Be Preserved." Paper written for

Aral-Caspian Committee, the Academy of Sciences, U.S.S.R. Moscow, 1965.

HAMMOND, R. PHILIP. *Agricultural Water by Nuclear Desalination and Technical Routes to Its Achievement.* Paper presented at University of Arizona Symposium on Water Production Using Nuclear Energy. Tucson, Arizona, March 30–April 1, 1966.

HEWITT, A. A., and FURR, J. R. "Influence of Salt Source on the Uptake of Chlorides by Selected Citrus Seedings." *Proceedings, American Society for Horticultural Science,* Vol. 86, 1965.

HEWITT, A. A., FURR, J. R., and CARPENTER, J. B. "Uptake and Distribution of Chlorides in Citrus Cuttings During a Short-Term Salt Test." *Proceedings, American Society for Horticultural Science,* Vol. 84, 1964.

HILL, GLADWIN. "Desalting Plants Spurred on Coast," *The New York Times,* August 14, 1966.

HIRSHLEIFER, JACK, DEHAVEN, JAMES C., and MILLIMAN, JEROME W. *Water Supply: Economics, Technology and Policy.* Chicago: University of Chicago Press, 1960.

Ionics, Inc. *Water.* Watertown, Massachusetts, 1967.

"Israel Announces a Desalting Plan," *The New York Times,* December 1, 1967.

JESSEL, B. B. "Is Desalination Really Necessary?" *Israel Youth Horizon,* Vol. III, No. 5, Jerusalem, 1966.

KLYACHKO, VITALY. "The Fresh Water Problem in the Soviet Union," *Novosti Press Agency,* Moscow, U.S.S.R., 1966.

KNEESE, ALLEN V., and SMITH, STEPHEN C. *Water Research.* Baltimore, Maryland: Johns Hopkins Press, 1966.

KRONBERGER, H. *Desalination of Water: Development in the United Kingdom.* Paper presented at the Tokyo meeting of the World Power Conference, October 16–20, 1966.

KUCHEL, THOMAS H. "From Dust to Dust: A Legislator's View of California's Coming Water Crisis," *San Diego Law Review,* June, 1967.

League of Women Voters of the United States. *Population + Production = Pollution.* Washington, D.C., 1965.

LEITNER, GORDON F. *Design Features of the World's Largest Flash Type Desalting Plant at Tijuana, Mexico.* Address to the Tenth National Symposium of the Instrument Society of America, May 8, 1967.

LOEBEL, FRED A. *Industrial Water Reclamation Developments.* Address to the American Public Works Congress, Boston, Massachusetts, October 2, 1967.

LOSEV, B. "Water, Water Everywhere Everywhere? But . . . ," *Sputnik,* Moscow, U.S.S.R., 1966.

LUDWIGSON, JOHN. "Water International," *Science News,* Washington, D.C., May 27, 1967.

MALLAN, LLOYD. "Slaking the World's Big Thirst," *INCO Magazine,* International Nickel, Co., Inc., New York, 1966.
MANN, DEAN E. *Political Implications of Migration to the Arid Lands.* Paper presented at the 133d Meeting, American Association for the Advancement of Science, Washington, D.C., December 29, 1966.
MOSS, FRANK E. *The Water Crisis.* New York: Frederick A. Praeger, 1967.
MUMFORD, LEWIS. *The City in History.* New York: Harcourt, Brace & World, 1961.
NACE, RAYMOND L. "Water in Flatland," *International Water Engineering,* October, 1966.
NIKOLAIEFF, GEORGE A. (ed.) . *The Water Crisis.* New York: H. H. Wilson, 1967.
North American Water and Power Alliance. *NAWAPA.* Ralph M. Parsons Company, Los Angeles, California, 1965.
"Polymers to Freshen Water," *Soviet Life,* Washington, D.C., July, 1965.
POPOV, NIKOLAI. "Face Lifting on a Grand Scale," *Soviet Life,* Washington, D.C., August, 1966.
PREHN, W. LAWRENCE, and SIGAFOOS, ROBERT A. *"The Potential Contribution of Desalting to Future Water Supply in Texas.* Report prepared for the Texas Water Development Board and the U.S. Office of Saline Water.
Ralph M. Parsons Company. *Water Management.* Los Angeles, California, 1967.
RAMEY, JAMES T. *Progress and Problems in Nuclear Desalting.* Remarks at the Inter-American Conference on Economic and Technical Aspects of Nuclear Power Generation in Latin America, Puerto Rico, February 25, 1965.
"Salty Waters," *Resources,* Resources for the Future, Washington, D.C., January, 1967.
Saudi Arabian Ministry of Agriculture and Water, Saline Water Conversion Office. *Saudi Arabia Harnesses Its Resources for Progress, Prosperity and Peace.* Jedda, May, 1967.
SCHUL, ZE'EV, "New Plans See Larger U.S.–Israel Joint Desalination Project," *The Jerusalem Post,* November 20, 1967.
SEABORG, GLENN T. *Future Outlook for the Application of Nuclear Science.* Address at a symposium in celebration of the Maria Sklodowska-Curie Centenary, Warsaw, Poland, October 19, 1967.
SMITH, GENE. "Atomic Desalting Under Study Here," *The New York Times,* May 25, 1968.
SOMOV, NIKOLAI. "Taming the Desert," *Soviet Life,* Washington, D.C., August, 1966.
SPORN, PHILIP. *Fresh Water from Saline Waters.* Oxford, England: Pergamon Press, 1966.
SULLIVAN, WALTER. "Desalting Water," *The New York Times,* June 28, 1964.

————. "Tahal's Water Plan, Reaching the Limit by 1971," *The Jerusalem Post*, January 30, 1967.

United Nations. Food and Agricultural Organization. *Report of the World Food Congress*. FAO, Rome, Italy, 1963.

United Nations Educational, Scientific and Cultural Organization. *Adaptation of Ruminant Animals to Variation of Salt Intake*, by D. A. DENTON, J. R. GODING, R. SAVINE, and R. D. WRIGHT, University of Melbourne. Paper presented at the Teheran Symposium on Salinity Problems in the Arid Zones. UNESCO, Geneva, Switzerland, 1961.

United Nations. International Atomic Energy Agency. *Costing Methods for Nuclear Desalination*. IAEA, Vienna, Austria, 1966.

U.S. Agency for International Development. Office of Engineering. *The Sun—The Sea—And Fresh Water—Solar Distillation Technology*. Washington, D.C., November, 1966.

U.S. Congress. House. *Authorization of Saline Water Conversion Program*. 90th Cong., 1st sess., May 1, 1967, *Congressional Record*.

U.S. Congress. House. Committee on Interior and Insular Affairs. *Providing for the Participation of the Department of the Interior in the Construction and Operation of a Large Prototype Desalting Plant in California*. Rept. 180, 90th Cong., 1st sess., April 7, 1967.

U.S. Congress. House. Committee on Interior and Insular Affairs. Statement before the committee by Frank C. DiLuzio, Director, Office of Saline Water, February 28, 1966.

U.S. Congress. House. *Participation of the Department of the Interior in the Construction and Operation of a Large Prototype Desalting Plant in California*. H. R. 439, 90th Cong., 1st sess., April 20, 1967, *Congressional Record*.

U.S. Congress. House. *Report Authorizing Appropriation for Saline Water Conversion Program*. Washington, D.C., April 24, 1967.

U.S. Congress. House. Subcommittee on Irrigation and Reclamation. *Metropolitan Water District Desalting Plant*. Hearings before subcommittee, February 27–28, 1967, 90th Cong., 1st sess. Washington, D.C., Government Printing Office, 1967.

U.S. Congress. Senate. Committee on Foreign Relations. Statement before the committee by Stewart L. Udall, Secretary of the Interior, October 19, 1967.

U.S. Congress. Senate. Committee on Interior and Insular Affairs. *Authorizing Appropriations for the Saline Water Conversion Program, Expanding the Program, and for Other Purposes*. S. Rept. 210, 90th Cong., 1st sess., May 8, 1967.

U.S. Congress. Senate. Committee on Interior and Insular Affairs. Statement before the committee by Frank C. DiLuzio, Assistant Secretary for Water Pollution Control, U.S. Department of the Interior, September 19, 1966.

U.S. Congress. Senate. Committee on Interior and Insular Affairs. Statement before the committee by Robert A. Skinner, Metropolitan Water District of southern California, September 19, 1966.

U.S. Congress. Senate. Subcommittee on Irrigation and Reclamation. *Saline Water Conversion.* Hearings before the subcommittee, May 18–19, 1965, 89th Cong., 1st sess., Washington, D.C.: Government Printing Office, 1965.

U.S. Department of Agriculture. Agricultural Research Service, Beef Cattle Research Branch. *Effects of Level of Sodium Chloride Consumption on Water and Mineral Balance in Beef Cattle.* Report by C. J. ELAM and L. K. AUTRY. No date.

U.S. Department of Agriculture. *Water: The Yearbook of Agriculture.* Washington, D.C.: Government Printing Office, 1955.

U.S. Department of the Interior. Office of Saline Water. *A-B Seas of Desalting.* Washington, D.C., 1967.

U.S. Department of the Interior. Office of Saline Water. *Operating Experiences at the OSW East Coast Test Facility, Wrightsville Beach, North Carolina.* Report by WALTER L. BARNES and WILFRED J. HAHN. No date.

U.S. Department of the Interior. Office of Saline Water. *Saline Water Conversion.* Washington, D.C.: Government Printing Office, 1962.

U.S. Department of the Interior. Office of Saline Water. *Saline Water Conversion Report,* for the years 1953–1966. Published annually.

U.S. Department of the Interior. "The Population Challenge . . . What It Means to America," *U.S. Department of the Interior Conservation Yearbook No. 2,* Washington, D.C., 1966.

University of Arizona. Environmental Research Laboratory. *Controlled-Environment Agriculture for Coastal Desert Areas.* Tucson, Arizona, July, 1967.

URROWS, GRACE M. *Nuclear Energy for Desalting.* U.S. Atomic Energy Commission, Washington, D.C., 1966.

VELZY, CHARLES R., and VELZY, CHARLES O. "Unique Incinerator Develops Power and Provides Salt Water Conversion," *Public Works Magazine,* Ridgewood, N.J., April, 1964.

"Water, Our Most Abused Resource," *Senior Scholastic,* October 7, 1965.

Water Desalination: Proposals for a Costing Procedure and Related Technical and Economic Considerations. New York: United Nations, 1965.

Water Desalination in Developing Countries. New York: United Nations, 1964.

"Water from the Sea for the Industries of Southern California," *Western Manufacturing,* San Francisco, May, 1967.

"Water in Industry," *Resources,* Resources for the Future, Washington, D.C., May, 1967.

Water Research Association. *"Desalination as a Supplementary Water Resource.* Medmenham, England, 1967.

Weir Westgarth, Ltd. *Floating Fresh Water Factories.* Glasgow, Scotland, 1967.

Westinghouse Electric Corporation. Water Province Department. *Water: Pure and Simple.* Orange, California, 1967.

WILEY, A. J.; AMMERLAAN, A. C. F.; and DUBEY, G. A. *Application of Reverse Osmosis to Processing of Spent Liquors from the Pulp and Paper Industry.* Research Conference on Reverse Osmosis, San Diego, California, February 13–15, 1967.

"World's Largest Flash Evaporator Nears Completion in Key West," *Power Engineering,* 1967.

Worthington Corporation. *Water.* New York, 1967.

YEMELYANOV, VASILY. "Water Desalting: A Field for Cooperation," *Soviet Life,* Washington, D.C., October, 1965.

The following papers were presented to the First International Symposium on Water Desalination, October 3–9, 1965, Washington, D.C.

BARNEA, JOSEPH, United Nations. *Water Costs in Developing Countries.*

CALVIT, B. W., and SLOAN, J. J., Office of Saline Water, U.S. Department of the Interior. *Operation Experience of the Webster, South Dakota, Electrodialysis Plant.*

DATTAL, R. L.; GOMKALE, S. D.; AHMED, S. Y.; and DATAR, D. S., India. *Evaporation of Sea Water in Solar Stills and Its Development for Desalination.*

DELYANNIS, A., and PIPERGLOU, E., Technical University, Athens, Greece. *Solar Distillation in Greece.*

EL-SAIE, M. H. ALI. *Water Production Experience of the City of Kuwait.*

FREUTH, HANS, Germany. *Cost Determination and Comparison of Nuclear and Fossil Fueled Dual-Purpose Power and Desalination Plants.*

HASHIZUME, MASAO. *Utilization of Desalinated Water in Japan.*

HOWE, EVERETT D., University of California. *General Review of the Work of the Sea Water Conversion Laboratory at the University of California.*

KORYAKIN, YU.; LOGINOV, A. A.; MIKHAN, V. I.; and MONCHINSKY, A. G. *Use of Reactors of the Beloyarsk AEPS Type for Dual-Purpose Desalination Plants.*

KORYAKIN, YU., and LOGINOV, A. A. *Analysis of Technical and Economic Indicators of Nuclear Power Desalination Plants.*

KRONENBERGER, H. *Objectives of the United Kingdom Research and Development Programme for Desalination.*

MAKINSKY, I. Z. *The Power Desalination Plant in the City of Baku.*

MEIGS, PEVERIL, International Geographical Union. *Coastal Deserts: Prime Customers of Desalination.*

MEREDIEU, J. DE, Food and Agriculture Organization. *Irrigation with Desalinated Water.*

PELED, ABRAHAM. *Operation of the Freeze Desalination Plant at Eilat, Israel.*

POWELL, SHEPPARD T. *Factors Involved in the Economic Production of Usable Fresh Water from Saline Sources.*

REICHLE, LEONARD F. C. *Evaluation of All Potential Sources of Energy for Desalting.*

SCHROEDER, HANS JURGEN. *Operational Experiences with the Sea Water Conversion Installation at Taranto, Italy.*

SERGEYENKO, I. L. *Analysis of the Economics of Large Capacity Thermal Desalination Plants.*

SMITH, ANDREW C. *Some British Achievements in Desalination.*

STEWART, JAMES M. *Some Practical Aspects of Desalination by Evaporation.*

SUÁREZ, JORGE, and PLIEGO, JOSÉ M. *Desalination in Spain.*

VILENTCHUK, I., Sea Water Conversion Commission, Israel. *Survey of Water Desalination in Israel.*

YAGODIN, G., International Atomic Energy Agency. *Co-ordination of International Research on Nuclear Desalting.*

ZAOSTROVSKY, F. P.; NOVIKOV, E. P.; SHATSILLO, V. G.; GOLUB, S. I.; CHERNOZUBOV, V. B.; and TKACH, B. I. *Distillation Desalination Plant in the City of Shevchenko—Layout, Equipment and Operating Experience.*

The following papers were presented to the Second European Symposium on Fresh Water from the Sea, Athens, May 9–12, 1967.

AHMED, S. Y.; GOMKALE, S. D.; DATTA, R. L.; and DATAR, D. S., Central Salt and Marine Chemicals Research Institute, India. *Scope and Development of Solar Still for Water Desalination in India.*

BOM, P. R., Werkspoor-Amsterdam, the Netherlands. *Large-Scale Seawater Desalination in the Netherlands.*

DAVISON, R. R., Texas A & M University. *A Solvent Extraction Desalination Pilot Plant.*

DELYANNIS, A., and PIPERGLOU, E., Technical University, Athens, Greece. *The Patmos Solar Distillation Plant.*

ENGLISH, J. M., and EL-RAMLY, N., University of California. *Economic Evaluation of Desalting Sub-system as a Part of the Total Water System.*

GARK, S. K.; GOMKALE, S. D.; DATTA, R. L., and DATAR, D. S., Central Salt and Marine Chemicals Research Institute, India. *Development of Humidification-Dehumidification Technique for Water Desalination in Arid Zone of India.*

GOLUB, S. I.; SERGENKO, I. L.; SOBOLEV, E. A.; CHERNOZUBOV, V. B.; SHATSILLO, V. G.; TKACH, B. I.; TOKMANTSEV, N. K.; and MUSIKHIN, N. N., State Committee on the Use of Atomic Energy, U.S.S.R. *Comparison of Economic Data of the Main Types of Desalting Plants.*

HAMMOND, R. PHILLIP, U.S. Atomic Energy Commission. *The Nuclear Desalination Program at the Oak Ridge National Laboratory.*

JOHNSON, K. D. B., and CLELLAND, D. W., United Kingdom Atomic Energy Agency. *Mobile and Floating Flash Distillation Plants.*

LOEB, S., and SELOVER, E., University of California. *Potable Water for Coalinga, California, by Reverse Osmosis: Sixteen Months of Field Experience on a Five Kilo-Gallon Tubular Plant.*

MAWER, P. A., Water Research Association. *The Economics of Multistate Flash Distillation in Relation to Conventional Water Supply.*

STARMER, R.; THORNLEY, J. D.; and MODET, J. A. *Problems Likely To Be Encountered in the Design of Large Flash Distillation Plants.*

ZUCKERMAN, N., Israel Electric Corporation, Ltd. *The Eilat 1,000,000 GPD, MSF Distillation Plant—Operating Experience.*

The following papers were presented to the International Conference on Water for Peace, May 23–31, 1967, Washington, D.C.

ABBAS, B. M., Government of Pakistan. *Planning Water Development for Irrigation, Flood Control and Navigation in Pakistan.*

ACKERMAN, EDWARD A., Carnegie Institution of Washington. *Policy Considerations in Planning and Development: The United States Experience.*

AL FAISAL, PRINCE MOHAMED, Director, Sea Water Desalination, Ministry of Agriculture and Water, Saudi Arabia. *Desalination Program for Saudi Arabia.*

ANAYA, MANUEL, Mexican Hydraulic Resources Secretariat. *Mexico and Its Water Resources.*

ANGELINI, ARNALDO M., Ente Nazionale per L'Energia Elettrica. *Prospects of Multi-purpose Hydro Plants for Coverage of Future Fresh Water and Electric Power Requirements in Italy.*

ATESHIAN, K. H., and MOHAMED, I. S., Bookers Sugar Estates, Ltd., Guyana. *Re-use of Water in the Sugar Industry in Guyana.*

BARNEA, JOSEPH, United Nations. *Water Policy from the United Nations Point of View.*

BENASSINI, OSCAR, Department of Water Resources, Mexico. *Program of Studies for the Irrigation Project.*

BONIS, SAMUEL B., Instituto Geográfico Nacional, Guatemala. *A basic Critique of Foreign Assistance Programs in the Light of Guatemala's Present Water Needs.*

BRICE, D. B., and YASHIN, D. A., International Atomic Energy Agency. *Selection of Nuclear Reactors for Desalination.*

BURGAUD, J. L., and OGER, C., Société Saint-Gobain Techniques Nouvelles. *Industrial Waters: A Method for the Study of Problems of Each Industrial Site.*

CADWALLADER, E. A., and WILSON, J. R. *Guidelines for Determining Feasibility of Desalination.*

CANDAU, M. G., Director-General, World Health Organization. *Water for Living.*

CARBALLOW, JORGE W., Servicio Nacional de Acueductors y Alcantarillado, Costa Rica. *Importance of the Economic Feasibility of the Potable Water and Sewerage Projects.*

CARTER, W. A.; SCHULTHEISS, H.; SALAZAR, E.; and SUAREZ GUZMAN, R., Inter-American Development Bank. *Financing Water Projects in Latin America.*

CRAHAY, LT. GENERAL A. E., Royal Commissioner for Water Problems, Belgium. *Influence of Industrialization on Water Problems.*

DA COSTA, JOSÉ A., United Nations Educational, Scientific and Cultural Organization. *The International Hydrological Decade: A Progress Report.*

DAVIES, EDWARD, Sierra Leone. *Problems Related to Water Resources Development in the Wet Tropics.*

DAVIS, W. K. Bechtel Corporation. *Sea Water Conversion as an Alternate Water Source.*

DERIENZO, P., and EVANS, ROBERT E., Burns & Roe, Inc. *A 2.5 MFG Universal Desalting Plant Design.*

DILUZIO, FRANK C., Assistant Secretary for Water Pollution Control, U.S. Department of the Interior. Remarks to closing session of the conference.

DOUGLASS, EDWARD F., Peace Corps. *Ingenuity and Water Supply: A Do-It-Yourself Approach.*

DOXIADIS, CONSTANTINOS. *Water and Human Environment.*

GOLZE, ALFRED R., Department of Water Resources, State of California. *Comprehensive Water Development in California.*

GRASSI, CARLOS J., Organization of American States. *Factors Affecting Irrigation Efficiency and the Contribution of Agricultural Engineering in the Improvement of Water Use in Latin-American Irrigation Projects.*

HAGAN, ROBERT M.; HOUSTON, CLYDE E.; and BURGY, ROBERT H., University of California. *More Crop per Drop: Approaches to Increasing Production from Limited Water Resources.*

HAGOOD, MEL A., Food and Agriculture Organization. *Water Management for Successful Irrigation.*

HAMMOND, R. PHILIP, Oak Ridge National Laboratory, U.S. Atomic Energy Commission. *Desalted Water for Agriculture.*

HASSLER, FRIEDRICH, Technische Hochschule, Darmstadt, Germany. *The Utilization of Water in the Qattara Depression.*

HOLLIS, MARK D., Pan American Health Organization. *Rural Community Water Supplies: A Discussion in Financing.*

HOLTON, H. T., Metropolitan Water District of Southern California. *The World's First Large Nuclear Desalting Plant: A Description of the Dual Purpose Plant To Be Located on a Man-made Island off the Coast of Southern California.*

HOWE, EVERETT D., Sea Water Conversion Laboratory, University of California. *Solar Distillation for Augmenting the Water Supply on Low Islands.*

HUNTER, JACK A., Office of Saline Water, U.S. Department of the Interior. *Advances in Desalting Technology.*

JOHNSON, LYNDON B., President of the United States. Remarks to conference.

JORDÁN, DAVID HERRERA, and FRIEDKIN, JOSEPH F., International Boundary and Water Commission, United States and Mexico. *The International Boundary and Water Commission, United States and Mexico.*

KATZ, WILLIAM E., Ionics, Inc. *The State of the Art in Electrolysis, 1967.*

KRONBERGER, H., United Kingdom Atomic Energy Authority, and SILVER, R. S., Glasgow University. *The Role of Desalination in Water Supplies.*

KRUL, W. F. J. M., Technological University, Delft, the Netherlands. *Water Problems of Humid and Sub-humid Zones.*

LEBOUSQUET, MAURICE, World Health Organization. *Health Aspects of Water Resources Development.*

MALETIC, JOHN T., Bureau of Reclamation, U.S. Department of the Interior. *Irrigation, A Selective Function: Selection of Project Lands.*

MATZ, R., Negev Institute for Arid Zone Research, Israel. *Application of Electrodialysis in Israel.*

MISHARI, H. E., Minister of Agriculture and Water, Kingdom of Saudi Arabia. *Toward Full Water Utilization in Saudi Arabia.*

MORSE, R. N., Commonwealth Scientific and Industrial Research Organization, Division of Mechanical Engineering, Melbourne, Australia. *The Potential for Solar Distillation in Australia.*

Netherlands Government Institute of Sewage Purification and Waste Treatment. *State of Water Pollution in the Netherlands.* Unsigned.

NORWOOD, GUS, Northwest Public Power Association. *Public Objectives in Water Resources Development.*

NOYAN, KEMAL, and ŞENOĞULLARI, TURHAN, Ministry of Energy and Natural Resources, Turkey. *Domestic and Industrial Water Supply Project for the City of Istanbul and Adapazari-Izmit-Istanbul Industrial Zone.*

OKUN, DANIEL A., and McJUNKIN, FREDERICK E., University of North Carolina. *Planning and Developing Water Supply Programs in Developing Countries.*

OLIVIER, H. *Irrigation as a Factor in Promoting Development.*

PARTRIDGE, EVERETT P., and PAULSON, E. G., Calgon Corporation. *Too Costly To Throw Away! Closed-Cycle Reuse of Water by Industry.*

PASSINO, ROBERTO, National Research Council, Italy. *Study and Research Activities of the Italian National Research Council in the Field of Water Problems.*

PRINDLE, RICHARD A., U.S. Public Health Service. *Health Significance of Water Quality.*

QUINTELA, ROBERTO M., University of Buenos Aires, Argentina. *The Possibilities for Desalting Water in Argentina.*

RAMEY, JAMES T., U.S. Atomic Energy Commission. *Policy Considerations in Desalting and Energy Development and Utilization.*

RAO, K. L., Ministry of Irrigation and Power, India. *Planning and Development of Water Resources in India.*

RASALAN, SANTOS B., Philippines Fisheries Commission. *Salt Water Encroachment—A Major Problem Today.*

REGGIORI, A.; SONGA, T.; and MAGRI, V., Instituto di Ricerche Breda, Milan, Italy. *Research Activity of the Breda Group in the Fields of Water Science and Technology.*

ROMULO, CARLOS P. *Man's Control of Water.*

SEN, R. B., Director-General, Food and Agriculture Organization. *Water for Food.*

SHIPMAN, HAROLD R., International Bank for Reconstruction and Development. *Considerations Involved in the Planning, Organization, and Design of Public Water Supplies.*

SHOAIB, MOHAMED, Vice President, International Bank for Reconstruction and Development. *Remarks to the conference.*

SHUVAL, HILLEL, Hebrew University, Israel. *Public Health Implications of Waste-Water Utilization.*

SPIEWAK, I., and EBEL, R. A., Oak Ridge National Laboratory, U.S. Atomic Energy Commission. *Cost Projections for Large Desalting Systems with Various Types of Couplings.*

SPORN, PHILIP, and GERBER, ABRAHAM. *The Social-Economic Evaluation of Water Resource Projects.*

STOYER, RAY L., Santee County Water District, California. *The Development of "Total Use" Water Management at Santee, California.*

TAYLOR, FLOYD B.; LONG, WILLIAM N.; MADDIX, F. DONALD; and HUGHES, P., U.S. Public Health Service. *Economic and Social Benefits from Improving Health by Provision of Safe Drinking Water Supplies.*

TIMMONS, JOHN F., and DOUGAL, MERWIN D., Iowa State University. *Economics of Water Quality Management.*

UDALL, STEWART L., Secretary of the Interior. Remarks to the conference.

VALENTE, M. NETO, Overseas Ministry, Portugal. *The Hydrology of Cape Verde and Water for Peace.*

VILENTCHUK, I., Sea Water Conversion Commission, Israel. *Desalted Water for Israel's Agriculture.*

WAGNER, CARRUTH J., U.S. Public Health Service. *Benefit-Cost Analysis: A Method To Demonstrate the Importance of Water Resources Development.*

WARRELL, E. G., Snowy Mountains Hydroelectrical Authority, Australia. *Snowy Mountains Hydroelectric Scheme, Australia.*

WIENER, AHARON, Tahal—Water Planning for Israel, Ltd. *Comprehensive Sectoral Planning of Irrigated Agriculture in Developing Countries.*

——— *Organizations for National Water Programmes.*

WILLIAMS, DONALD A., Soil Conservation Service, U.S. Department of Agriculture. *Modern Water Management To Assure Needed Supplies in a Peaceful World.*

YARON, D., Hebrew University, Israel, and BRESLER, E., Ministry of Agriculture, Israel. *Towards Economic Evaluation of Water Quality in Irrigation.*

YOUNG, GLADWIN E., Soil Conservation Service, U.S. Department of Agriculture. *Agriculture's Responsibilities and Opportunities To Ensure Clean Water.*

There are two desalination newsletters that provide an excellent picture of the changing and expanding desalting field. They are good resources of both background and current information, and were used extensively in the preparation of this book. They are

Desalting Digest. Published monthly by Sci/Tech Digests, Inc., Washington, D.C.

Water Desalination Report. Published weekly by Richard Arlen Smith, Washington, D.C.

Index

Abbott Laboratories, 100
Abdullah al-Salim al-Sabah, 135
Abqaiq, Saudi Arabia, 141
Ackerman, Edward A., 41
Acre, Israel, 144
Aegina Island, 45, 46
Africa, 71
al-Hasa, Saudi Arabia, 139
Al-Khafji, Saudi Arabia, 141
Al-Khobar, Saudi Arabia, 99, 141
Alaska, 27
Anand, D. R., 52
Anaya, Manuel, 149–50, 151
Ancón, Ecuador, 95
Antigua, 12, 133
Appleton, Wisconsin, 99
Aqua-Chem, Inc. (Milwaukee), 49, 97, 148, 186
Arabs, and distillation, 3–4
Arad, N., 36
Argwingskodhek, C. M. G., 156
Aristotle, 3
Arizona, 28, 29
Arrecife, Canary Islands, 43
Aruba, Netherlands Antilles, 4, 73, 90, 91, 184–85
Ashdod, Israel, 147, 189
Assab, Ethiopia, 129
Athens, Greece, 47
Atomic Energy Commission, 20–21, 178
Australia, 11, 12, 24, 66, 133; desalination for food-growing processes in, 69; salt-toleration tests on stock animals in, 74; solar distillation plant in, 92–93

Aztec civilization, 150
Azusa, California, 99

Bahamas, 96, 128
Bahrein, 91, 128
Baity, H. G., 116
Baja California, Mexico, 28, 50, 71, 131, 149
Baldwin-Lima-Hamilton firm, 4, 37
Barcelona, Spain, 94
Bari, Italy, 51
Barnea, Joseph, 78–79, 106–10, 118–19, 159
Basil, St., 3
Belgium, 88–89, 93
Bermuda, 12, 90, 97, 128, 133, 168
Biemiller Andrew J., 101
Big Sandy River, 90
Bihar, India, 53
Bolsa Chica Island, 59, 62, 163, 182
Bombay, India, 54
Bonis, Samuel B., 111
Bowen, William, 169
Bower, C. A., 74
Boyko, Hugo, 75–76
Brackish water, 11, 26, 27, 38, 75
Bradley, Charles C., 41
Brazil, 12, 133
Brice, D. B., 187
British Ship Research Association, 31
British Water Research Association, 10
Brooklyn, New York, 100
Brownsville, Texas, 57
Buckeye, Arizona, 57
Burgaud, J. L., 102